CAPITALIZATION AND PUNCTUATION

Intermediate

by

Arnold F. Checchi

ISBN 978-0-89187-205-4
©1997, 1987, 1981, 1974—Curriculum Associates, Inc.
North Billerica, MA 01862

15 14 13 12 11 10

NOTES TO THE STUDENT

CAPITALIZATION AND PUNCTUATION—INTERMEDIATE is a language mechanics skillbook that will help you learn to use capital letters and punctuation marks correctly. This skillbook has six parts:

Contents The contents is your personal record of the lessons you will be asked to do, where they are found, and how well you do them.

Pretests You will take a pretest for each lesson to find out what you know and what you need to learn.

Lessons The thirty-five lessons present to you, one at a time, the rules about capital letters and marks of punctuation and samples to show you how to use them. Each lesson has a part to learn and a practice and review of what you have already learned.

Answers After you have done the practice and the maintenance exercises, use the answers to correct your work.

Dictations For each lesson, there are two sets of dictation exercises that will give you more practice in what you have learned.

Post Tests You will take a post test after lessons 4, 10, 13, 18, 23, 29, 32, and 35 to review the completed lessons.

USING THE BOOK

1. The teacher will give you a pretest—actually a number of small quizzes—for what is to be learned in each of the thirty-five lessons.

2. The pretest will be corrected by the teacher. The teacher will mark your contents to show you which lessons you will do to help you learn something that is giving you difficulty. You will skip the lessons you already know.

3. Study "I—Learning Exercise." If you are working with a partner, read this material aloud. Read it again if you don't understand. Study what has been done in the sample sentences. There is no written work here, but the lesson should be well studied.

4. Study "II—Practice Exercises." This is a writing activity that will show whether or not you understand what the lesson is about. Next is "III—Maintenance Exercises," which is a review of what you learned in earlier lessons. If you are working with a partner, each of you should do your own writing, working alone, and then compare what each of you has done. If your work is identical, it is probably correct. If your work is not uniform, explain to one another why you did what you did. Make changes in your work if you wish. If your answers are still different, wait until you correct the exercises.

5. Turn to the answers in the back of the book and correct your written work. Circle each error and write the correct answer beside it. Count your correct answers. Turn to your contents. Write that number in the circle.

Read the two numbers as a fraction to see how well you've learned the lesson.

6. Turn to the dictation for the lesson. Dictate a set of sentences to your partner. Have him or her dictate the second set of sentences to you. Correct the work together, using the sentences in the book.

7. After several lessons, you will be given a post test by the teacher, who will correct it. Each post test reviews all the lessons you have done. Your score can be written in the contents.

REMEMBER:

a. Put your newly learned rules to daily use in your written work.

b. Notice capital letters and punctuation marks in the things you read. Do you know the reasons for their use? Do they make reading easier for you?

CONTENTS

Testing Program:

Pretests 7-14
Post Tests.................123-128

Complete the lessons checked.   **Page**   **Score**

☐ **Lesson 1:**   Statements and Commands **15**

               Answers 95   ◯/32
               Dictations................. 115

☐ **Lesson 2:**   Questions and Exclamations **16**

               Answers 95   ◯/46
               Dictations................. 115

☐ **Lesson 3:**   The Interjection **18**

               Answers 95   ◯/75
               Dictations................. 115

☐ **Lesson 4:**   Abbreviations **20**

               Answers 96   ◯/65
               Dictations................. 115

☐ **POST TEST ONE** (Teacher Will Correct)   123   ◯

☐ **Lesson 5:**   Capitalizing Names and Initials ..   **22**

               Answers 96   ◯/87
               Dictations................. 115

☐ **Lesson 6:**   Titles Belonging to People **24**

               Answers 96   ◯/72
               Dictations................. 116

☐ **Lesson 7:**   Capitalizing Titles **25**

               Answers 97   ◯/159
               Dictations................. 116

☐ **Lesson 8:**   Capitalizing First Word of
               Every Line of Poetry.............   **28**

               Answers 97   ◯/73
               Dictations................. 116

Student's Name

Complete the lessons checked.   **Page**   **Score**

☐ **Lesson 9:**   Capitalizing Father and Mother .. **30**   ◯/59

               Answers 98
               Dictations................. 116

☐ **Lesson 10:**   Capitalizing "I" .... **32**   ◯/40

               Answers 98
               Dictations................. 116

☐ **POST TEST TWO** (Teacher Will Correct)   124   ◯

☐ **Lesson 11:**   Capitalizing Names of
               Companies and Stores .... **34**   ◯/135

               Answers 99
               Dictations................. 117

☐ **Lesson 12:**   Capitalizing Names of
               Buildings and Special Places .... **36**   ◯/88

               Answers 99
               Dictations................. 117

☐ **Lesson 13:**   Capitalizing Names of
               Clubs and Special Groups .... **38**   ◯/99

               Answers 100
               Dictations................. 117

☐ **POST TEST THREE** (Teacher Will Correct)   125   ◯

☐ **Lesson 14:**   Capitalizing Names of Days,
               Special Days, and Holidays ...... **41**   ◯/74

               Answers 101
               Dictations................. 117

☐ **Lesson 15:**   Capitalizing Names of Streets.... **42**   ◯/145

               Answers 101
               Dictations................. 118

☐ **Lesson 16:**   Capitalizing and Punctuating
               Names of Cities and States ...... **45**   ◯/131

               Answers 102
               Dictations................. 118

☐ **Lesson 17:**   Writing State Names .... **47**   ◯/168

               Answers 102
               Dictations................. 118

Complete the lessons checked.   **Page**   **Score**

☐ **Lesson 18:**   Capitalizing Names of Countries
                   and Nationalities ....   **50**   ◯/107

                        Answers   103
                        Dictations................   118

☐ **POST TEST FOUR** (Teacher Will Correct)   125   ◯

☐ **Lesson 19:**   Last Names First in Lists .... **53**   ◯/110

                        Answers   104
                        Dictations................   118

☐ **Lesson 20:**   Commas With Words in Series and
                   Groups of Words in Series .... **55**   ◯/118

                        Answers   104
                        Dictations................   119

☐ **Lesson 21:**   Commas With "Yes" and
                   "No" ....   **57**   ◯/97

                        Answers   105
                        Dictations................   119

☐ **Lesson 22:**   Commas With Conjunctions .....   **59**   ◯/85

                        Answers   106
                        Dictations................   119

☐ **Lesson 23:**   Commas in Appositives..........   **62**   ◯/60

                        Answers   106
                        Dictations................   119

☐ **POST TEST FIVE** (Teacher Will Correct)   126   ◯

☐ **Lesson 24:**   The Comma in Address ....   **65**   ◯/68

                        Answers   107
                        Dictations................   120

☐ **Lesson 25:**   Direct Quotations at the
                   Ends of Sentences ....   **67**   ◯/136

                        Answers   107
                        Dictations................   120

☐ **Lesson 26:**   Direct Quotations at the
                   Beginnings of Sentences .... **70**   ◯/156

                        Answers   108
                        Dictations................   120

Student's Name

5

Complete the lessons checked.   **Page**   **Score**

☐ **Lesson 27:**   The Interrupted Quotation ....   **73**   ◯ /188

                    Answers   109
                    Dictations.................   120

☐ **Lesson 28:**   The Indirect Quotation ....   **75**   ◯ /158

                    Answers   109
                    Dictations.................   121

☐ **Lesson 29:**   Writing Conversation ....   **77**   ◯ /145

                    Answers   110
                    Dictations.................   121

☐ **POST TEST SIX** (Teacher Will Correct)   127   ◯

☐ **Lesson 30:**   The Apostrophe in Contractions   **80**   ◯ /117

                    Answers   111
                    Dictations.................   121

☐ **Lesson 31:**   The Apostrophe in Singular
                    Possessives ....   **83**   ◯ /65

                    Answers   111
                    Dictations.................   121

☐ **Lesson 32:**   The Apostrophe in Plural
                    Possessives ....   **86**   ◯ /130

                    Answers   112
                    Dictations.................   122

☐ **POST TEST SEVEN** (Teacher Will Correct)   128   ◯

☐ **Lesson 33:**   Capitalizing Geographical Terms
                    (Rivers, Oceans, Mountains,
                    and Continents) ....   **89**   ◯ /68

                    Answers   113
                    Dictations.................   122

☐ **Lesson 34:**   Capitalizing Geographical Terms
                    (Regions and Sections) ....   **91**   ◯ /59

                    Answers   113
                    Dictations.................   122

☐ **Lesson 35:**   The Colon ....   **93**   ◯ /169

                    Answers   114
                    Dictations.................   122

☐ **POST TEST EIGHT** (Teacher Will Correct)   128   ◯

Student's Name

PRETEST

LESSON 1   **Directions:** Punctuate the following sentences.

    a.   The boy walked with his sister

    b.   Sit closer to the table

    c.   The veterinarian examined the dog

    d.   Telephone your father and ask him if you can stay later

    e.   Get plenty of rest on school nights

LESSON 2   **Directions:** Punctuate the following sentences.

    a.   Do you ever watch television

    b.   Help

    c.   May I have my allowance early this week

    d.   Where is the wastebasket

    e.   Look out for that car

LESSON 3   **Directions:** Punctuate the following sentences.

    a.   Oh look at the sunset

    b.   Ah it's such a clear day for the picnic

    c.   For goodness sake where did you find that

    d.   Well I'm not really sure

    e.   Help The boat's sinking

LESSON 4   **Directions:** Abbreviate the underlined words.

    a.   <u>Mister</u> Alexander J. Henning

    b.   <u>Captain</u> G. Westcott Lowell, <u>United</u> <u>States</u> <u>Navy</u>

    c.   5 <u>feet</u> 7 <u>inches</u>

    d.   <u>Monday</u> <u>Tuesday</u> <u>Wednesday</u> <u>Sunday</u>

    e.   <u>February</u> <u>May</u> <u>October</u> <u>December</u>

PRETEST

LESSON 5   **Directions:** Capitalize and punctuate where necessary.

a.   Treasurer j c cronin bought some exciting gifts for the bazaar.

b.   My dog spot plays with rusty's cat dash.

c.   Who wrote the initials "j c s" on this paper?

d.   p t lanson phoned bonita durán this afternoon.

e.   I have j pierpont morgan's autograph under nelson rockefeller's.

LESSON 6   **Directions:** Capitalize where needed.

a.   A photograph of secretary of defense dylan appeared.

b.   yoshio jones, a boy scout, accepted the task.

c.   town moderator jasmine nesbitt pounded her gavel.

d.   He spoke to president wilson of our club.

e.   Does prince albert play rugby?

LESSON 7   **Directions:** Capitalize, punctuate, and underline where necessary.

a.   Have you read the shattered skull by Carol Perkins?

b.   The book faster and faster by Robert Froman had some excellent material.

c.   The girl spoke in a loud voice as she gave her report titled wool of

the world.

d.   My report, bees, servants of humans is due Monday.

e.   My report on bees is due Monday.

LESSON 8   **Directions:** Capitalize where necessary.

> the jungle
>
> what a fracas,
>
> what a riot!
>
> is the jungle
>
> never quiet?
>
> will the macaws
>
> not ever cease
>
> to screech and scream?
>
> is there no end
>
> to all this green?   Mary Britton Miller

PRETEST

LESSON 9   **Directions:** Capitalize where necessary.

    a.   Show your excellent paper to mother.

    b.   Show your excellent paper to my father.

    c.   Our father and mother have left for Jamaica.

    d.   Will grandmother come for the holidays?

    e.   I wonder if grandfather saw my brother.

LESSON 10   **Directions:** Capitalize where necessary.

    a.   May i have a piece?

    b.   Last night i went to bed early.

    c.   My mom and i played ball.

    d.   Will i need a ticket?

    e.   I told you i didn't have one.

LESSON 11   **Directions:** Capitalize where necessary.

    a.   My uncle works for chariot motor company.

    b.   They are having a CD sale at the music box.

    c.   Have you been to the norton shoe factory since it was remodeled?

    d.   Are eggs less expensive at budget market or at economy depot?

    e.   The minneapolis insurance company is located in Realty Park.

LESSON 12   **Directions:** Capitalize where necessary.

    a.   The new heritage center, which opened recently, is across the street from the majesty hotel.

    b.   The polk free library is adjacent to the tubman school.

    c.   Some high-school students are playing in the baseball league.

    d.   The eiffel tower is about 400 feet taller than the washington monument.

    e.   Our class visited the zoo at the charlotte city park last Tuesday.

PRETEST

LESSON 13   **Directions:** Capitalize where necessary.

a. We saw Garrin play with the steelers of the pee wee football league.

b. My mother is a member of the klondike hospitality committee and the chicago garden club.

c. Will you be able to come to the girl scouts meeting?

d. My uncle served with the royal canadian air force and the united states marines.

e. Members of the safety patrol get to see the yankees play in the spring.

LESSON 14   **Directions:** Capitalize where necessary.

a. football game at thanksgiving

b. first monday in september

c. last day of vacation

d. valentine's day

e. new year's day and halloween

LESSON 15   **Directions:** Capitalize where necessary.

a. new mexico avenue

b. edmunds road

c. ohio turnpike

d. route 135

e. storrow drive

LESSON 16   **Directions:** Capitalize and punctuate where necessary.

a. cedar hills maine

b. new york city new york

c. toronto ontario

d. fort lauderdale florida

e. san diego california

P
R
E
T
E
S
T

Name _____

PRETEST

LESSON 17   **Directions:** Write correctly the two abbreviations for these states.

		(standard)	(postal)
a.	Texas	_____	_____
b.	Tennessee	_____	_____
c.	California	_____	_____
d.	New Hampshire	_____	_____
e.	Oregon	_____	_____

LESSON 18   **Directions:** Capitalize where necessary.

a.   english-speaking person

b.   chinese cooking

c.   united arab emirates

d.   the dutch of south africa

e.   french pastry

LESSON 19   **Directions:** Alphabetize the following names, using last names first.

a.   juanita hernandez

b.   mariam bradley

c.   lee pappas

d.   f e ferguson

e.   austin j roberts

LESSON 20   **Directions:** Punctuate the following sentences where necessary.

a.   Lyle Ben and Craig are on the Steelers.

b.   She spoke in a clear loud and forceful voice.

c.   Neatness accuracy and speed are characteristics of good work habits.

d.   Sarah looked under the chair behind the divan and in the box for her letter.

e.   They jumped sprinted or leaped over the obstacles.

LESSON 21   **Directions:** Punctuate the following sentences where necessary.

a.   No I don't think so.

b.   Yes it's cold today.

c.   No the library program is being held this afternoon.

d.   Yes we have bananas.

e.   Yes we have our gloves on.

PRETEST

LESSON 22   **Directions:** Rewrite the following pairs of word groups in each example into a single sentence. Add words and punctuate where necessary.

     a.   The teacher spoke. We didn't hear the directions.

     b.   Carmelita caught the ball. She threw it to first base.

     c.   We will be swimming. We will be diving.

     d.   The lights changed. We drove on.

     e.   I will be drinking. I will be eating.

LESSON 23   **Directions:** Punctuate where necessary.

     a.   Ryan the gardener enjoys skin diving.

     b.   We visited Plimoth Plantation a reconstruction of the first New England settlement.

     c.   Charlotte the sympathetic spider spun her web again.

     d.   Albert Schweitzer the Belgian medical missionary died years ago.

     e.   Mr. Woodruff the principal discussed bicycle safety with the class.

LESSON 24   **Directions:** Punctuate where necessary.

     a.   Dana where is my spinning reel?

     b.   After you write your headings class go right to work.

     c.   Do you know how to sail Carolyn?

     d.   Cynthia and Ted please collect the papers.

     e.   The bicycle is in the garage Shelly.

LESSON 25   **Directions:** Capitalize and punctuate where necessary.

     a.   Tony said show me where you put it

     b.   The girls asked is your sister going to the rally

     c.   Frank exclaimed what a great time we had

     d.   Joan answered it's right here where I put it

     e.   The teacher reminded please form a single line

LESSON 26   **Directions:** Capitalize and punctuate where necessary.

     a.   come on down invited Ian MacDonald

     b.   we are leaving the day after tomorrow announced Father

     c.   will we meet during the vacation asked Darcy

     d.   i always have trouble starting the car on wet days explained Mother

     e.   look over the bridge exclaimed Jill

PRETEST

LESSON 27   **Directions:** Capitalize and punctuate where necessary.

   a.   look reminded the kangaroo before you leap

   b.   the next time moaned Albert I won't use glue until I have all the parts ready

   c.   when asked Deirdre will you be coming home

   d.   she ran through the yard she said and opened the door

   e.   if the phone rings again muttered Bob I'm not going to answer it

LESSON 28   **Directions:** Punctuate the following sentences where necessary and capitalize.

   a.   sam asked his grandmother if he could go

   b.   jackson replied that he liked the assembly

   c.   she asked if one-word answers were accepted

   d.   the policeman told Jocelyn which way to go

   e.   the teacher reminded the children to pass in their homework

LESSON 29   **Directions:** Correct the conversation. Use a separate piece of paper.

I saw a strange gray bird in our yard today said Rico to the children in his class

how big was the bird asked Alice it was about twenty inches long replied Rico

Kevin asked was it gray all over well Rico answered the bird's back was gray but

its stomach was yellow, and it had an orange spot on its head Glen asked if the

bird's tail was gray the bird's tail was black Rico said its wings were dark grayish

brown

LESSON 30   **Directions:** Write contractions for the following groups of words.

   a.   do not   _____

   b.   will not   _____

   c.   had not   _____

   d.   you will   _____

   e.   who is   _____

   f.   it is   _____

   g.   let us   _____

   h.   that is   _____

   i.   they would   _____

   j.   are not   _____

PRETEST

LESSON 31   **Directions:** Punctuate the following sentences where necessary.

a. Nicoles sister is taller than she is.

b. Irenes dog is spotted.

c. Is the squirrels tail bushy?

d. The boys voice is shrill.

e. The soldiers helmet had a huge dent.

LESSON 32   **Directions:** Punctuate the following sentences where necessary.

a. The childrens play received good notices.

b. Giraffes necks are quite long.

c. Are all ducks feet webbed?

d. Deers tracks are smaller than those of antelopes.

e. The fire fighters coats were covered with ashes.

LESSON 33   **Directions:** Capitalize where necessary.

a. mississippi river

b. amazon river

c. mt. washington

d. the winding brook

e. north american wildlife

LESSON 34   **Directions:** Capitalize where necessary.

a. southeastern kentucky

b. sailed due east

c. the south

d. driving west

e. western section

LESSON 35   **Directions:** Write the following times correctly *in numbers*.

a. three thirty in the afternoon   _____

b. seven fifteen in the morning   _____

c. half past eleven in the morning   _____

d. ten minutes of six in the evening   _____

e. quarter of eight in the evening   _____

Lesson 1   Statements and Commands

I. LEARNING EXERCISE

> You have learned there are four kinds of sentences. Only two of these end with a period. They are:
>
>   a.   Statement—A **statement** is a sentence that tells something. It **begins** with a capital letter and **ends** with a period (.).
>
>   Sample: *We ate tacos at the party.*
>
>   *The windows were found broken.*
>
>   b.   Imperative—These sentences give **commands**. They tell you to do something. These **commands** also begin with a **capital letter** and end with a **period**.
>
>   Sample: *Please stand next to your partner.*
>
>   *Bring me your books.*

II. PRACTICE EXERCISES

A. The following sentences are statements and commands. Put the proper capital letters and punctuation in the proper places. The first one is done for you.

1.   Mary went shopping for her grandmother.

2.   we arrived at the hardware store together

3.   the noisy pet show was more fun than the hobby fair

4.   sit in the front seat

5.   the school nurse drove me home

6.   the exciting holidays are now over

7.   telephone your mother and tell her you'll be late

8.   run to the end of the soccer field

9.   the faithful dog was sitting at its master's feet

10.   get to bed early

B. The paragraph below contains **seven sentences**. Insert the capital letters and periods to make the sentences into a corrected paragraph. Make the corrections right on this paragraph below.

one May morning Maria was riding to school on her bicycle it was a bright sunny day

suddenly she saw some broken glass in the street near the curb she was worried that it would

cause someone some trouble quickly Maria got off her bicycle and picked up all of the glass

she saw a big trash basket and dropped in the broken glass Maria had done her good deed for

that day

Total Possible Correct: 32

(See page 95.)

III. PAIRED DICTATION Turn to page 115.

Lesson 2   Questions and Exclamations

I. LEARNING EXERCISE

You have learned that the **statement** and **command** each begin with a capital letter and end with a **period**. The **question** and **exclamation** begin with a **capital letter**, but each ends in a different manner.

a. Question—   The **question** is a sentence that asks something. It ends with a **question mark** (?).

   Sample: *Did your brother bake this bread?*

   Which subject do you enjoy most in school?

b. Exclamation—The kind of sentence which shows **surprise** or **strong feeling** is called an **exclamation**. An exclamation ends with an **exclamation mark** (!).

   Sample: *Oh boy! I found my newspaper money!*

   Be careful of that car!

II. PRACTICE EXERCISES

Below are ten sentences. Some are questions and some are exclamations. Remember your rules for punctuating and capitalizing these sentences. Read the sentences. Insert the capital letters and proper ending marks of punctuation where needed. The first one is done for you.

1. **D**
    ~~d~~id you see the dancing elephant on TV**?**

2. do you have a partner

3. a man just landed by parachute in the back yard

4. are you going with us to the game

5. what a noisy jet that is

6. did Anthony wash the chalkboard

7. what tricks can your dog do

8. look out

9. help

10. someone is robbing the bank now

III. MAINTENANCE EXERCISES

The following sentences need to begin and end correctly. Do the work right on the paper.

1. what did Ann suddenly see in front of her

2. at first we were not entirely sure

3. how horrible

4. was that Libby up there

5. the secretary was making an announcement

6. the choir was seated in the rear of the auditorium

7. my brother sings with a group

8. she kept watching

9. be here in time to help

10. my friend snores loudly

11. she is diving in to save her

12. they left immediately

13. answer one more question

14. did you know the skunk was there

Total Possible Correct: 46

(See page 95.)

IV. PAIRED DICTATION
Turn to page 115.

Lesson 3   The Interjection

I. **LEARNING EXERCISE**

Maybe you have heard conversation like this after a hard test in school:

> **Whew**! That last one was hard.
>
> **Quiet**! I'm not through yet.
>
> **Oh**, is that the answer?
>
> **No**, it isn't.
>
> **Yes**, it is.
>
> **Well**, I'm really surprised.
>
> **Good-by**, I'm leaving.

You can see that each sentence above has an exclamatory word in it—this word is **underlined**. We call each exclamatory word an **interjection**. Pronounce the word:

in-ter-jec-tion

An **in-ter-jec-tion** is a word that is used to express surprise, alarm, delight, or other strong feeling. Discuss the following with your group.

1. What mark of punctuation do you find after each interjection in the sentences above?
2. Which two sentences show stronger feeling?
3. Which sentences show milder feeling?

Remember:

1. An interjection that shows strong feeling is followed by an exclamation mark. The next word begins with a capital letter.

2. An interjection that shows mild feeling is followed by a comma. The next word usually does not begin with a capital letter.

Sometimes an interjection is used in the middle of a sentence, as:

Keith, **wow**, you've grown!

What marks separate the interjection from the rest of the sentence?

II. PRACTICE EXERCISES

Correct the following sentences on this paper. Insert all capital letters and marks of punctuation where needed. Remember your rules for interjections.

1. hurrah we are ready

2. great they're here at last

3. oh I've forgotten the bat

4. look it's behind you

5. my you're quiet

6. well I'm glad we have it

7. yes I agree with you

8. congratulations you won

9. hurray the game is over

10. ouch these shoes hurt

III. MAINTENANCE EXERCISES

A. Correct the following sentences on this paper.

1. when will you be ready

2. sit still in the canoe

3. the sunrise will be early tomorrow

4. look at the rocket

5. i went to the market

6. what fun we had

7. did you see the planet Venus

8. we had a spelling test yesterday

9. oh the clowns were the most fun

10. another clown had a hat two feet high

B. Insert question marks, periods, and exclamation marks where they are needed below. Correct words that should begin with capital letters.

we had a wonderful time at the fair last week it was a thrilling experience for the whole

family we had never camped out before the first night my sister kept me awake because she

heard funny sounds the next night we were given strict orders we were told to go right to

sleep do you suppose we did as a matter of fact we were so tired after the long day that we

fell right to sleep we have already begun to make plans for next year's fair

Total Possible Correct: 75
(See page 95.)

IV. PAIRED DICTATION   Turn to page 115.

Lesson 4   *Abbreviations*

I. LEARNING EXERCISE

We often use **abbreviations** such as **Mr.** for **Mister**, **Dr.** for **Doctor**, and **Co.** for **Company**. An **abbreviation** is a short way of writing a long word. **Some** abbreviations **must begin** with a **capital letter**.

Samples: Abbreviations of titles used with names, times, and places require a **capital letter** and a **period**.

Mr. Eban	*Mister Eban*	*Pres.* Wilson	*President Wilson*
Feb.	*February*	*U.S.*	*United States*
Wed.	*Wednesday*	*St.*	*Street*

Some abbreviations do not need capital letters at the **beginning**, but **periods must follow them**. Abbreviations for weights, measures, and other units (other than *in.* for *inch*) **do not** take periods. Note that the abbreviation is the same in the singular and the plural.

oz	*ounce* (or *ounces*)	*lb*	*pound* (or *pounds*)
in.	*inch* (or *inches*)	*tel.*	*telephone*
mi	*mile* (or *miles*)	*hr*	*hour* (or *hours*)
wk	*week* (or *weeks*)	*yr*	*year* (or *years*)
no.	*number*	*bldg.*	*building*

Remember:

Miss is **not** an abbreviation and does not end with a period.

Miss does begin with a capital letter.

Ms. is a title given to a woman who may be married or unmarried. *Ms.* is **not** an abbreviation, but does begin with a capital letter and end with a period.

When an abbreviation falls at the end of a sentence, an additional period to end the sentence is not needed. When the end punctuation to the sentence is a question mark or an exclamation mark, insert the mark after the period in the abbreviation.

II. PRACTICE EXERCISES

A. Correct the following abbreviations by putting in the proper capital letters and periods. Do the work on this paper.

1. mrs Rosa Ciani

2. 16 in

3. mr Calvin Washington

4. pres Abraham Lincoln

5. 24 Woodward ave or 5 Lee st

6. mon or fri or sat

B. Below are two columns. Match the abbreviations in Column A with the word it is the abbreviation for in Column B by drawing lines. Capitalize and punctuate the abbreviations as required. One is done for you.

A.	B.
1. doz.	1. pound
2. tues	2. number
3. lb	3. September
4. no	4. foot or feet
5. ave	5. dozen
6. mr	6. Road
7. dr	7. Doctor
8. sept	8. Tuesday
9. ft	9. Mister
10. rd	10. Avenue

III. MAINTENANCE EXERCISES

Find the sentences in the following short paragraph. Underline each letter that should be written as a capital, and insert the punctuation marks where needed.

nick came running into the house he asked if his father was getting ready nick's father put his coat on and turned off the stove it would be too late to get the book he needed at the library nick's teacher assigned a special report to be done in three weeks he wanted to get an early start on it what luck they had a flat tire on the way the town hall clock was striking six nick and his father arrived just as the doors to the library were being locked what do you suppose was Nick's fate he got the last copy of the book he wanted have you ever had a close call like this one

Total Possible Correct: 65
(See page 96.)

IV. PAIRED DICTATION   Turn to page 115.

DO NOT DO THE NEXT LESSON—TAKE POST TEST ONE

Lesson 5   Capitalizing Names and Initials

I. LEARNING EXERCISE

The names of all **people** and **pets** begin with a **capital letter**. When initials are used in place of names, they are capitalized.

Remember **always** to place a period (.) **after every initial**.

Sample: *John **H**. **P**eters*

J. Henry Peters

J. H. Peters

*My dog **B**enny can do many tricks.*

II. PRACTICE EXERCISES

Correct the following sentences. Insert all capital letters above the letters to be capitalized and insert marks of punctuation where needed. Remember all the rules for capitalization and punctuation you have learned so far when making your corrections. Do your work on this paper.

1. eileen novak made a good speech

2. a meeting of the club was held by karl after school

3. ms levy suggested that we have a party

4. what a lively discussion leroy led

5. yesterday jane eastman was reading the school paper

6. it was suggested by olga and elena that we have a field day next week

7. chiang's name was written on the chalkboard

8. did yvonne ask about her dog nibs

9. the order was signed by mr san miguel

III. MAINTENANCE EXERCISES

A. Capitalize the following sentences as needed. Insert all capital letters above the letters to be capitalized. Put in punctuation where needed. Do your work on this paper.

1. father left yesterday to interview ms a j bauer

2. the invitation said I was to bring a gift

3. in my letter I said I would bring some things to the party

4. tom and I went to see mrs nora c riley

5. I called dr j r pappas to the scene of the accident

6. we have tickets for the hockey game

B. In the short paragraph below you are to decide where the capital letters and punctuation marks should go. Make the corrections on this paper. Remember what you have learned.

An Apple a Day

last Sunday Mother, Father, and I drove to the country on our way we stopped to visit mr boudreau mother told me he is editor of a magazine mother used to work for him he gave my mother and father two boxes of apples to take home I ate apples until I couldn't eat any more dr brown was called to treat me I found out that too many apples a day can bring the doctor instead of keeping her away dr brown agreed with me

Total Possible Correct: 87
(See page 96.)

IV. PAIRED DICTATION   Turn to page 115.

Lesson 6 — Titles Belonging to People

I. LEARNING EXERCISE

The titles belonging to people begin with capital letters.

Sample: *President Jefferson*

or

Pres. Jefferson

II. PRACTICE EXERCISES

Place capital letters and punctuation where needed in the following sentences.

1. the nurses were pleased when dr russo was named to the staff of Mercy Hospital

2. a recommendation will be read by senator eckstein or representative johnson

3. are you expecting a check signed by treasurer calhoun today

4. has president schmidt signed the new law

5. general broadbent will be in town today to review the parade

III. MAINTENANCE EXERCISES

A. Write the abbreviations for the days of the week. Capitalize, punctuate, and spell correctly.

_____

_____

B. Write the abbreviations for the months of the year. (Remember that there are no abbreviations for three months of the year.)

_____

_____

MAINTENANCE EXERCISES (continued)

C. In the short paragraph below you are to decide where the capital letters and punctuation marks should go. Make the corrections on this paper. Remember what you have learned.

it was April 1 my brother and I went to the deli we arrived about 3 P.M. and had sandwiches when we were through, I told him I didn't have a cent this was an April Fool's joke he cried, "oh no you must have." as it turned out neither of us had any money have you ever been embarrassed like this

Total Possible Correct: 72

(See page 96.)

IV. PAIRED DICTATION Turn to page 116.

Lesson 7 — *Capitalizing Titles*

I. LEARNING EXERCISE

By now you have written a few book reports. Are you giving proper attention to capital letters in your titles? Look at these titles of books!

The Little House in the Big Woods

Cattle Trails in the Old West

Which words begin with capital letters?

LEARNING EXERCISE (continued)

Remember these three rules:

1. Use a capital letter to begin the **first word**, the **last word**, and **each important word** in the title of a book, story, or poem.

2. Underline the title of any book, magazine, or newspaper. In print, these titles are italicized.

   Homer Price by Robert McCloskey (book)

   Newsweek (magazine)

   Monitor (newspaper)

3. Enclose titles of reports, songs, and poems in quotation marks.

   "Insects of the Americas" (report)

   "The Star-Spangled Banner" (song)

   "To a Skylark" (poem)

NOTE: Words like *a, an, the, and, but, or, in, of, to, on,* and *for* are not **important words.** These words **do not begin** with a capital letter, except when used as first or last word in a title.

II. PRACTICE EXERCISES

A. Write the following titles and authors correctly.

1. across america on an emigrant train by jim murphy

2. the wind in the willows by kenneth grahame

3. the hubble space telescope by gregory vogt

4. the pelican chorus by edward lear

5. missing may by cynthia rylant

6. the summer of the swans by betsy byar

7. charlotte's web by e b white

8. a string in the harp by nancy bond

B. In the following sentences are some titles of reports, songs, poems, and books. Underline them as needed. Capitalize the correct letters in the entire sentence and add the necessary punctuation. Do not rewrite. Do the work on the sentences in the space provided.

1. jill read the book entitled harriet tubman for her report

2. the class is reading the historical novel johnny tremain by esther forbes

3. the report exploration of mars is available in the library

4. our class song is entitled together and is from the songbook america

5. my favorite poem is a dream deferred by langston hughes, which last year appeared in a

   magazine called youth

6. is the poem scenes of summer published in today's herald recorder

7. please turn to the song home on the range in music for young singers

III. MAINTENANCE EXERCISES

A. On the line before each item write the abbreviation of the word underlined. Remember to place capitals and periods where necessary in the abbreviation and in the item itself.

_____ 1. mister arnold e banelow   _____ 5. senator cecilia sanchez

_____ 2. doctor esther b levine   _____ 6. general dexter carlton

_____ 3. 15 East Clark street   _____ 7. december 1999

_____ 4. 884 Fenton avenue   _____ 8. governor oliver winslow

B. In the following short paragraph decide where capital letters and punctuation are needed.

it was a cold February Sunday dr casey began shoveling out her driveway I looked out of my

front window and noticed her working fast my neighbor, capt horace williams from the

Chicago Police Department, began helping her I decided something must be wrong, so I went

out to help we all worked for one hour to get dr casey on her way to the hospital an accident

had occurred on Winter Street, and three people required her help what excitement this

caused

Total Possible Correct: 159
(See page 97.)

IV. PAIRED DICTATION   Turn to page 116.

Lesson 8

Capitalizing First Word of Every Line of Poetry

I. LEARNING EXERCISE

The following poem will show you two rules to follow when writing a poem. Read it. Look at it carefully.

Only My Opinion

Is a caterpillar ticklish?
Well, it's always my belief
That he giggles, as he wiggles
Across a hairy leaf.

Monica Shannon

Answer questions:

1. How is the title written?
2. How does each line of the poem begin?

II. PRACTICE EXERCISES

A. The following are short poems. Check the title and each line of poetry. Put capital letters above the small letters that need to be capitalized.

jonathan gee	looking up
jonathan gee	jonathan gee
struck at a bee;	has troubles to spare;
a sadder and wiser	he walks, you see,
boy is he.	with his nose in the air.
he's nursing a sting	jonathan gee
that burns like fire,	with his mind in a muddle
and has put his beehive	watched a bud in a tree
out for hire.	and fell into a puddle.

28

B. Copy the following poem observing all that you have learned in this lesson.

a limerick

there was a proud man from the coast

who happily sat on a post.

but when it was cold,

he relinquished his hold

and called for some warm milk and toast.

_____

_____

_____

_____

_____

_____

_____

III. **MAINTENANCE EXERCISES**

A. Rewrite the following titles correctly on the space provided under each printed one. Review your rules for writing titles of stories, books, reports, poems, songs, etc.

1. a talking hound (story)

   _____

2. an army of fleas (book)

   _____

3. time on my hands (song)

   _____

4. the umbrella by the door (poem)

   _____

5. doctor dolittle's zoo (book)

   _____

6. a lesson for andy (story)

   _____

7. high flight (book)

   _____

8. winter song (poem)

   _____

B. Look in the sentences below for the interjections. Remember what you have learned. Decide where the interjections are and how you will punctuate them.

1. Oh I'm sorry I'm late.

2. Hurray our team won!

3. Wait we will be right there.

4. Oh I broke my glasses.

5. Ouch I cut my fingers.

6. Horrors did he fall?

Total Possible Correct: 73

(See page 97.)

IV. PAIRED DICTATION Turn to page 116.

 Lesson 9   Capitalizing Father and Mother

I. LEARNING EXERCISE

> **Always** when words like *mother* and *father* appear in your writing as **names**, they **must begin** with a **capital letter.** Do **not** use a capital when a **modifying** word (my, our, a, the, their) is used with the words *father* and *mother*.
>
> Samples: *Show your paper to **G**randmother.*
>
> *I went to the wedding with **F**ather and **M**other.*
>
> *I went to the beach with **my** father and mother.*

II. PRACTICE EXERCISES

Remember your new rule above. Remember, too, the rules you have learned in the previous lessons. Correct the letter below. Put in all capital letters, periods, exclamation and question marks needed.

dear grandmother,

thank you very much for inviting me to visit with you both mother and father have agreed to

let me go may I come the last week of June my father will see to it that I get the noon train I

will arrive at 2:30 how I'm looking forward to seeing you and grandfather mother and father

send their love to everyone

Your grandchild,

_____

(your name)

III. MAINTENANCE EXERCISES

A. Proofread the following poems and insert the capitalization correctly.

first star

star light, star bright,

first star I've seen tonight.

I wish I may, I wish I might,

have the wish I wish tonight.

Anon.

the butterfly

up and down the air you float

like a little fairy boat;

I should like to sail the sky

gliding like a butterfly.

Clinton Scollard

MAINTENANCE EXERCISES (continued)

B. Below is a review of capital letters and punctuation of exclamations, questions, and titles of stories and reports. How is each sentence to be corrected? Put capital letters above the small letters needing to be capitalized, and insert the punctuation where needed.

1. are you reading sounder for your book report

2. he just disappeared through the ice

3. we just finished hearing the teacher read danger is my business by h craig

4. aren't you the next person in line

5. ow you're hurting me

6. do you find this exercise easy

7. the report entitled graphing data was written by a group of mathematicians

Total Possible Correct: 59

(See page 98.)

IV. PAIRED DICTATION Turn to page 116.

Lesson 10   *Capitalizing "I"*

I. LEARNING EXERCISE

> The letter *I* is **always capitalized** when used as a word.
>
> Samples: *Tom and **I** know an exciting story.*
>   *May **I** have the butter, please?*

II. PRACTICE EXERCISES

Correct each sentence below on this paper. Capitalize where necessary.

1. last night i saw a movie.

2. i said to my dad, "May i buy some popcorn?"

3. my report is called "when i was in the hospital."

4. the dog i have is called frisky.

5. i am going to the soccer game.

6. i was told to speak to our coach, ms yumi numata.

III. MAINTENANCE EXERCISES

Read the following sentences. Remembering what you have learned so far, insert the capital letters and punctuation marks where needed. Mark the capital letters above the small letters needing to be capitalized.

1. it is easy to take the train to Columbus

2. sit down before you fall down

3. mother and father surprised me on my birthday

4. do you live on Summer street or Winter avenue

5. my mother told me that father was going to take me skiing

6. have your tickets ready, please

7. i suggested that father and mother see the new show in town

8. we leave at 12:30 P.M. and arrive in Hartford four hours later

Total Possible Correct: 40

(See page 98.)

IV. PAIRED DICTATION   Turn to page 116.

DO NOT DO NEXT LESSON — TAKE POST TEST TWO

Lesson 11

Capitalizing Names of Companies and Stores

I. LEARNING EXERCISE

The names of companies and stores must always begin with a capital letter. All the important words in the name are capitalized.

Samples: (company) *They have worked for **G**eneral **A**utomation **C**ompany for years.*

(store) *Every January there is a sale at **C**ompuworld.*

NOTE: Sometimes companies are called corporations.
Their names are written with capital letters.
The word *the* before the name of a company or store is usually not capitalized.

II. PRACTICE EXERCISES

A. On the line provided write what you think would be a good name for a company or store. Remember the rules above.

Example: hardware store _____

1. food store _____

2. hobby store _____

3. card shop _____

4. clothing store _____

5. toy shop _____

6. drugstore _____

7. music store _____

8. furniture store _____

9. automobile company _____

10. florist shop _____

B. Insert capital letters where required in the following sentences. Put your corrections on this paper above the words to be capitalized. Insert punctuation marks where needed.

1. the united shoe company is one of the largest companies in our area

2. when we were in Philadelphia, i bought a coat at shopper's warehouse

3. i would like to be an engineer with lazeon corporation

4. she was in charge of the martinez advertising agency when she retired

5. did you go into catalina's when you were in Boston

6. i wrote to the canadian national railway for information for my report

7. my mother wrote a check to the charleston electric light company

III. MAINTENANCE EXERCISES

A. Remembering what you learned about capitalizing names of people, correct the following exercises by inserting the capital letters and punctuation marks where needed.

1. the initials j f k stand for president john fitzgerald kennedy

2. the thirty-fourth president of the united states was dwight d eisenhower

3. i read that the referee is to be ms carla l almeida

4. coach folger received permission from principal schmidt to begin baseball practice

5. lihwa chang, shelton little, shani marks, howard davis, and i made the first team

6. mary lou and i are going to the dance tonight

7. dr scott asked me if i could read the smallest print on the eye chart

8. i just read a great book called black stallion

B. The sentences below will review many things you have already learned. Correct them by inserting capital letters and punctuation marks in each sentence where they are needed.

1. i think that i might be asked to be a leader in Explorers

2. give my regards to your mother and your father

3. yea we won the championship

MAINTENANCE EXERCISES (continued)

4. the poem never the winner was written by elaine meyer

5. she told me that i might be featured in an article in tomorrow's tribune

6. his photograph appeared in an article in sports world

7. well we'll wait for the election results

8. officer tracey trains all staff at clarkson cleaners

Total Possible Correct: 135

(See page 99.)

IV. PAIRED DICTATION Turn to page 117.

Lesson 12   *Capitalizing Names of Buildings and Special Places*

I. LEARNING EXERCISE

In your story writing and letter writing you might mention the names of schools, public buildings, and special places. In doing so, always remember to **begin all important parts** of the **name** with **a capital letter**.

Samples: *Riverside School*
Ocean City Library
In Washington, D.C., I visited the Lincoln Memorial.

NOTE: The word *school* is capitalized when used in the name of a school.

II. PRACTICE EXERCISES

A. Complete the following sentences:

1. The name of the school I now attend is the _____

2. The name of the next school I hope to attend is the _____
_____

3. The name of our high school is the _____

4. Our local college is called _____

5. The tallest building in town is called the _____
_____

B. Rewrite the following using capitals correctly when necessary.

1. seattle chamber of commerce _____

2. the white house (in Washington, D.C.) _____

3. tulane university _____

4. fairmont park _____

5. high school _____

6. morgan country day school _____

7. bates college _____

8. yellowstone national park _____

9. library of congress _____

10. month _____

III. MAINTENANCE EXERCISES

A. Remembering all that you have learned, put the capital letters and punctuation in the following to make each correct. Do your work on this paper.

1. finnegan's book store

2. suki onuki, mgr, stop and spend co

3. mulligan's is located in New York

4. my sister has applied to mears, e m t schelf, and priceless for a job

5. the gas company sent booklets for my report

6. the whim-wham company has its headquarters in Atlanta

MAINTENANCE EXERCISES (continued)

B. Read the letter below very carefully. Some capital letters have been left out. Decide where they go and insert them above the small letters needing to be made into capitals. Punctuate wherever necessary.

dear indira,

    we just came home from fishing on captain bill's new boat i watched my cousins sit all day without catching a thing the owner of the boat, mrs consuelo t diaz, caught the longest fish it was the biggest cod i ever saw before we headed home my aunt and uncle let us dive into the water and swim what fun we had i hope you can come soon we could go fishing together

Your friend,

anna m weiss

Total Possible Correct: 88
(See page 99.)

IV. PAIRED DICTATION Turn to page 117.

Lesson 13 — Capitalizing Names of Clubs and Special Groups

I. LEARNING EXERCISE

> The **names** of **specific clubs** and **special groups** must always begin with **capital letters**.
>
> Samples: the *Girl Scouts* of *America*
> the *United States Marines*
> the *Steelers–Patriots* game

II. PRACTICE EXERCISES

A. Consider the following very carefully and put capital letters above the small letters of words that should begin with capital letters.

1. the entrance age to join cub scouts is seven.

2. the johnstown garden club will go to the flower show in Jackson in March.

3. we all belong to the ashmont achievement association.

4. the little league browns won the pennant.

5. the cincinnati nurses' aides association donates much time to help out at the hospital.

6. the braxton athletic league sponsors baseball, soccer, and basketball for the

   children in our community.

7. would you serve on the board of the richmond stadium authority?

8. a united states coast guard plane came to the rescue of the sailors.

B. Rewrite the following with capital letters where necessary.

1. fri. _____

2. coat of arms _____

3. the chagrin falls glee club _____

4. the atlanta archery team _____

5. the c. e. society _____

6. baby-sitters _____

7. the american heart and lung association _____

8. white sox _____

9. beginners' group _____

III. MAINTENANCE EXERCISES

A. For each of the general places in the left-hand column you are to write the name of a building or place on the line beside it. Remember your rules for capitalization of these proper names. The first one is done for you.

1. a park _____

2. a school _____

3. a hospital _____

4. a bank _____

5. a store _____

6. a hotel _____

7. a beach _____

8. a theatre building _____

9. a camp _____

10. a college _____

11. a well-known building in town _____

MAINTENANCE EXERCISES (continued)

B. The following is a list of titles of stories and reports. Remembering what you have learned, rewrite these titles correctly on the lines provided, using capital letters correctly.

a crazy halloween party

_____

headlights and taillights

_____

colonial furniture

_____

america's first president

_____

from tadpoles to frogs

_____

C. What is wrong with the way this poem is written? Decide what to do and rewrite it correctly on the lines provided.

the cobbler

_____
(Title)

crooked heels

_____

and scuffy toes

_____

are all the kinds

_____

of shoes he knows

_____

he patches up

_____

the broken places,

_____

sews the seams,

_____

and shines their faces

_____

e a chaffee

_____

Total Possible Correct: 99

(See page 100.)

IV. **PAIRED DICTATION**   Turn to page 117.

STOP   DO NOT DO NEXT LESSON — TAKE POST TEST THREE

Lesson 14

Capitalizing Names of Days, Special Days, and Holidays

I. LEARNING EXERCISE

When writing the names of **days**, **months**, **holidays**, and **special days**, be sure to **begin** each with a **capital letter**.

Samples: *This is the first Saturday in November.*
The Thanksgiving game was played in the rain.

II. PRACTICE EXERCISES

Place capital letters where needed. Cross out each letter to be changed and put the capital letter above it in the sentence. Punctuate where necessary.

1. we are expected to be home for thanksgiving

2. martin luther king day and new year's day are in the same month

3. it rained every sunday in april

4. they are going to sound like a fourth of july rocket

5. san jacinto day and kuhio day are celebrated only in certain states

6. we are planning a memorial day play

7. i am going to march in the veterans day parade

8. school always begins around labor day

III. MAINTENANCE EXERCISES

A. Rewrite the following names of groups and clubs using capital letters where necessary.

1. 4-h club _____

2. norfolk bay united fund _____

3. national education association _____

4. white sox _____

5. the football team _____

6. a stamp club   _____

7. e a haskell foundation   _____

8. midwestern running association   _____

9. a nest of robins   _____

10. m m king school safety patrol   _____

B. Use a capital letter at the beginning of sentences and a mark of punctuation at the end. Do your work on this paper.

luther burbank was an important scientist he was a horticulturalist, an expert on plants he

studied and taught people how to grow better vegetables and fruits he developed many new

plants for modern gardens and farms

Total Possible Correct: 74
(See page 101.)

IV. PAIRED DICTATION   Turn to page 117.

Lesson 15   *Capitalizing Names of Streets*

I. LEARNING EXERCISE

When writing the names of **streets, roads, avenues, boulevards, drives, ways,** etc., remember to **begin** these names with **capital letters.**

Samples: *Estella has lived on **N**ewbury **S**treet for years.*
*His cousin just moved to their new home on **R**iver **A**venue.*

The abbreviations of the words *street, road,* and *avenue* must be capitalized (St., Rd., Ave.) together with the actual name.

Remember: It is best not to use the abbreviations *St., Rd.,* and *Ave.* when writing sentences. It is acceptable to abbreviate these when writing a label or an address.

II. PRACTICE EXERCISES

A. Underline all letters in the following exercises that should be capital letters. Put punctuation in where needed.

1. fifth avenue is a main street in New York City

2. the club will meet at 52 trumble street on tuesday

3. kim wu lives at 34 pine street in Reno

4. the longest street in the town is girand avenue

5. when we were in Washington we stayed in a hotel on constitution avenue

6. shore drive was closed during highway construction

B. Begin and end the sentences in the paragraph below correctly. Insert all other marks you might need to make the paragraph correct. Put your corrections on this paper.

many streets are named for famous people and places roger williams avenue in Providence

was named after the founder of Rhode Island brown street was named for another famous

man in the state other cities name streets after people that is why almost every city has a

washington street

III. MAINTENANCE EXERCISES

A. Underline all the letters which should be capitalized. Put in all other punctuation where needed to make the paragraph correct.

dag moved to Hartford on columbus day on monday he went to school jason and tomas

met him at the door of the phillips school they brought him to ms johnson's room on her desk

was a schedule of basketball games to be played at the maynard school dag was excited

because he liked basketball he was glad he had moved to Hartford

B. Write these names of groups and places correctly.

langley nurses union _____

american youth soccer league _____

explorers club _____

emerson hospital _____

san francisco public library _____

hull house _____

C. Place capital letters where needed to make the sentences correct. Make your corrections above the word. Which words should be underlined?

1. little pear is a book about a boy from China.

2. the forest pool is a book about Mexico.

3. trees is a poem by j kilmer.

4. i am an American because i am a citizen of the United States of America.

Capitalize and punctuate the following abbreviations correctly on the lines provided.

prof _____ Jackson   sat _____

capt _____ Polanski   aug _____

supt _____ Cohen   mon _____

D. Read the paragraph below. Decide where the capital letters and punctuation marks are needed. Make these corrections right on the paper. Remember what you have learned.

red cross aid

on wednesday, february 4, 1996, we are packing a gift box for the junior red cross our class

is sending the gift from tileston school to Malaysia principal reynolds is asking the help of all

students in the school the tattler, our newspaper, has the story of our gift drive for our

Malaysian friends we will take our boxes to chairman white in the gateway hotel to have him

send them overseas we hope that by valentine's day we have many more boxes packed we

know that we can reach our goal of a box a day in february please help us out

Total Possible Correct: 145
(See page 101.)

IV. PAIRED DICTATION   Turn to page 118.

44

Lesson 16 — Capitalizing and Punctuating Names of Cities and States

I. LEARNING EXERCISE

When writing the names of cities and states or provinces, there are four things to remember:

1. The **city** and **state** or **province** both **begin** with a capital letter.
2. When the city **and** state are written **together**, a **comma** is placed **between** them.
3. When writing addresses in a sentence, use commas to separate names of **street, city**, and **state**.

NOTE: A comma is also placed between a city and country when written together. Those names begin with a capital letter.

Samples: 1. *Pierre comes from Montreal, Quebec.*
2. *We live in Beaufort, South Carolina.*
3. *Barbara moved to 13 Park Avenue, South Bend, Indiana.*

II. PRACTICE EXERCISES

Below are exercises that require capital letters and punctuation marks. Underline the letters needing capitalization, and put marks where needed.

1. have you ever been to hollywood california

2. we traveled from atlantic city new jersey, to portland maine, in eight hours

3. there is a statue of paul revere in boston massachusetts

4. almost eighty thousand people live in savannah georgia

5. many tourists travel to new york city

6. plimoth plantation is in plymouth massachusetts

7. the largest city in the Midwest is chicago

8. do you know delores gomez from san antonio texas

9. does your cousin live in pittsburgh pennsylvania

10. did i hear you say you were from hartford connecticut

11. there is a paris France, a paris maine, and a paris illinois

12. leo's new address is 36 cleveland road denver colorado

III. MAINTENANCE EXERCISES

A. Underline the letters in the following exercises that require a capital letter. Remember all the rules you have learned so far. Place punctuation where needed.

1. our troop will canvass dodge street, cabot street, and county way

2. short street is the shortest street in town

3. my address is 77 islington road auburndale arizona

4. who lives at 1600 pennsylvania avenue

5. the capital of our state is sacramento california

6. bounty way is the next street past winding river road

B. Correct the following sentences using capital letters and punctuation where needed. Make the corrections on this paper.

1. have you seen trixie yet

2. the electric bulb was invented by thomas a edison

3. get off that thin ice now

4. look at that hail come down

5. what is the story of our flag

6. our thirty-eighth president was gerald ford

Total Possible Correct: 131

(See page 102.)

IV. PAIRED DICTATION   Turn to page 118.

Lesson 17 — Writing State Names

I. LEARNING EXERCISES

The names of most states can be written three different ways.

Samples:
California
Calif. (standard abbreviation)
CA (postal abbreviation)

A. The names of states are written out completely when they stand alone, as in titles, and when they are used in phrases or sentences.

Samples:
"Alaska"
"Sunny New Mexico"

from Maine to California
My address is 8035 Elgin Street, Detroit, Michigan 48234.
Have you ever been to Alaska?

B. The standard abbreviation is normally used in lists or tables and in indexes.

Samples:

VICE PRESIDENTS OF THE
UNITED STATES

Name	Birthplace
John Adams	Quincy, Mass.
Thomas Jefferson	Shadwell, Va.
Aaron Burr	Newark, N.J.
George Clinton	Ulster Co., N.Y.

WIND SPEEDS IN THE
UNITED STATES

Station	Avg.	High
Savannah, Ga.	8.1	66
Spokane, Wash.	8.7	59
Toledo, Ohio*	9.5	72
Washington, D.C.	9.3	78

*Some states do not have standard abbreviations.

C. The postal abbreviation is a two-letter code used with a ZIP code number for mailing addresses. Both letters are capitals, and no period is used.

Samples:
Haskins Electronics Center
296 Belle Meade Street
Detroit, MI 48236

Dr. Felipa Marella
4635 Calle Del Ciervo, East
Tucson, AZ 85718

II. PRACTICE EXERCISES

A. Write the standard abbreviation for each of the following. Remember to use the correct capitalization and punctuation.

1. District of Columbia   _____

2. Georgia   _____

3. South Dakota   _____

4. New York   _____

5. Nevada   _____

6. New Jersey   _____

7. West Virginia   _____

8. North Carolina   _____

9. South Carolina   _____

10. Maryland   _____

B. Match the standard state abbreviations in Column A with the state postal abbreviation in Column B.

A		B	A		B
1. Ala.	_____	AK	14. Minn.	_____	MN
2. Alaska	_____	MS	15. Mont.	_____	OH
3. Ariz.	_____	MA	16. Nebr.	_____	MT
4. Ark.	_____	IL	17. Ohio	_____	NE
5. Del.	_____	DE	18. Okla.	_____	TX
6. Hawaii	_____	AR	19. Oreg.	_____	OK
7. Idaho	_____	MI	20. Pa.	_____	WY
8. Ill.	_____	HI	21. Tenn.	_____	OR
9. Ind.	_____	AZ	22. Tex.	_____	WI
10. Mass.	_____	MO	23. Utah	_____	PA
11. Mich.	_____	IN	24. Wash.	_____	WA
12. Miss.	_____	AL	25. Wis.	_____	UT
13. Mo.	_____	ID	26. Wyo.	_____	TN

C. Write each address using the correct capitalization, punctuation, and form.

1. sharron's diner   122 merchants row   rutland   vermont   05702

_____

_____

_____

2. ms laurie watson   251 main street   ellsworth   maine   04605

_____

_____

_____

3. mr juan valdez   755 homer avenue   kansas city   kansas   66101

_____

_____

_____

4. mrs lillian ryan   25 cottage street   pawtucket   rhode island   02860

_____

_____

_____

D. Read the letter below. Make any capitalization and punctuation corrections required. Remember all the rules you have learned.

849 old farm road

charlottesville virginia 22903

august 6, 1996

Dear louise,

i had such a great time with you and your family last week the tour of colo. and wyo. you

planned for me was really exciting and interesting

our family is looking forward to seeing you next summer when you come to conn. for our family

reunion

thank you again

Love,

joanne

III. MAINTENANCE EXERCISES

The sentences below review many things you have already learned. Correct them by inserting capital letters and punctuation marks.

1. paula pashko and susan douglas drove from california to d c in july

2. my address is 16 signal street rochester new hampshire 03867

3. are you going to work for the silver stationery company in north dakota

4. the lancaster booster club visited florida during thanksgiving vacation

5. yes i am leaving for summer camp in iowa on tuesday, june 24

6. i read the phantom tollbooth on the train to mexico

7. dr peabody's office is in the fraser medical building on abbott street

8. tell father that i do not want him to worry about me

9. will capt manuela e ramos lead the veterans day parade

10. when is grandmother arriving from new orleans louisiana

Total Possible Correct: 168

(See page 102.)

IV. PAIRED DICTATION   Turn to page 118.

 **Lesson 18** *Capitalizing Names of Countries and Nationalities*

I. LEARNING EXERCISE

When you write a noun that is the name of a country, the name of the people of a country, or the name of a language, begin the name with a capital letter.

The names of special groups of people also begin with capital letters.

Samples: *Those who live in Holland speak Dutch.*
The Spaniards landed in Central America.

Capitalize any adjectives formed from these names.

Samples: *Italian literature*
Turkish language

II. PRACTICE EXERCISES

A. Remembering the rules you've learned so far, underline each letter that should have a capital.

1. this country was explored by the english, french, and spanish.

2. red, orange, and yellow are found in mexican pottery.

3. the chinese eat more rice than any other food.

4. vincent was too young to join the stanley explorers club.

5. the puritans came to america so that they could worship freely.

6. the visitor spoke persian because she was from iran.

7. schoolchildren give money to the junior red cross.

8. the democrats won the last election.

9. many japanese children enjoy different holidays than we do.

B. Correct the following list by putting a capital where a capital belongs. The first one is done for you.

1. *E* english	11. players	21. mother's day
2. pilgrims	12. japanese	22. yemen
3. halloween	13. indians	23. rebels
4. people	14. social studies	24. germans
5. sioux	15. street	25. french
6. pets	16. americans	26. asia
7. girls	17. soldiers	27. puerto ricans
8. hispanics	18. brazilians	28. american history
9. russians	19. cape verdeans	29. french literature
10. alaskans	20. europeans	30. biology

III. MAINTENANCE EXERCISES

Correct the following addresses. Put your corrections right on this paper. Remember what you have learned.

1. mr andrew p polanski

   36 elm street

   felton delaware 19943

   _____

   _____

   _____

2. professor jesse a powers

   71 lincoln avenue

   trenton new jersey 08601

   _____

   _____

   _____

3. ms judy gex

   172 fergus road

   south bend indiana 46624

   _____

   _____

   _____

4. chief miguel fernandez

   2745 main street

   hayward california 94540

   _____

   _____

   _____

5. dr karen l root

   1545 roosevelt avenue

   tampa florida 33601

   _____

   _____

   _____

6. mrs buckley

   river drive

   groton connecticut 06340

   _____

   _____

   _____

Total Possible Correct: 107

(See page 103.)

IV. PAIRED DICTATION Turn to page 118.

DO NOT DO NEXT LESSON — TAKE POST TEST FOUR

Lesson 19   Last Names First in Lists

I. LEARNING EXERCISE

You have noticed how many names of people are printed and arranged in lists, indexes, and the telephone book. Last names are printed first, and the last names are arranged in alphabetical order.

Samples: *Aaron, J. P.*
Dennis, J. Leonard
Mills, Margaret Mary
Sameski, Jan R.
Tano, David

When you are writing names of people in lists, it is always best to write the last name first, followed by the rest of the name as it is commonly used. Remember, when you write names in this fashion, a **comma** always separates the last name and the rest of the name. Initials are always followed with a period. Study the examples above to see how names may be written. It is always considered acceptable to write a list of names in alphabetical order. This has been done for you in the above list of names.

II. PRACTICE EXERCISES

Rewrite the authors' names below in alphabetical order. Follow the rules given above. Remember to look at the last name of each author to decide where it comes in alphabetical order. The first two are done for you.

1. elizabeth j coatsworth   *Andersen, Hans Christian*
2. andrew lang   *Brink, Carol R.*
3. eleanor farjeon   _____
4. a a milne   _____
5. hans christian andersen   _____
6. howard pyle   _____
7. robert louis stevenson   _____
8. robert mcCloskey   _____
9. ruth sawyer   _____
10. carol r brink   _____
11. p g wodehouse   _____

III. MAINTENANCE EXERCISES

A. What is needed to correct the following exercises? Make your corrections right above each word, and insert punctuation where it is actually needed.

1. the irish flag is green, white, and orange

2. the san diego marine reserve is the name of a service organization

3. the american red cross is a helpful agency

4. the salvation army also gives aid to the needy

5. the french first settled in canada

6. is turkey in the Near East

7. china and japan are located in the Orient

8. my cousin will spend all summer in kenya studying african culture

9. valentine's day is celebrated on february 14

10. the smithsonian museum is in washington d c

B. Below are three "envelopes." Capitalize and punctuate the names and initials already printed there. On the remaining two lines you are to write in a street, number, city, state, and a ZIP code. Use capitals and punctuation correctly. Remember the rules for abbreviation of *street*, *road*, *avenue*, etc., if you use them.

1. mr raymond e martin   _____

   (address)   _____

   (city, state, ZIP)   _____

2. maura a powers, m d   _____

   (address)   _____

   (city, state, ZIP)   _____

3. mrs leona s lynch   _____

   (address)   _____

   (city, state, ZIP)   _____

Total Possible Correct: 110
(See page 104.)

IV. PAIRED DICTATION   Turn to page 118.

Lesson 20

Commas With Words in Series and Groups of Words in Series

I. LEARNING EXERCISE

Sometimes it is necessary to include a list of words in a series. A series is a group of more than two words written together.

Sample: *Mother, Sister, and Brother were in the house at the time.*

When this occurs, a comma (,) is placed **between** these words. Notice that a comma **does not** follow the last word in the series, but does come before *and*. Study the following:

Samples: *Our flag is red, white, and blue.*
Did you hear the flutes, violins, cellos, and drums?

(A comma always separates more than two groups of words in a series.)

Sample: *The boy dashed across the field, through the orchard, and down the road.*

II. PRACTICE EXERCISES

All of the following sentences contain words or phrases in a series. Separate these series with commas. Use your rules for punctuation and capitalization.

1. kate tina and lisa are on the team

2. mark did his work quickly neatly thoroughly and correctly

3. the coach gave her team a short interesting and inspiring talk

4. the cats were chased across the street through the gate past the yard and into the house

5. wool cotton and silk are woven here

6. the peaches are large ripe sweet and juicy

7. the workers can knit spin weave and sew

8. the hikers walked down the path through the field and over the bridge

9. the visitors arrived in a large new streamlined car

10. there is enough food for you harry and me

III. MAINTENANCE EXERCISES

A. Arrange the following names in alphabetical order with the last name first. Use the correct capitalization and punctuation. Write your names in order on the lines provided.

1. william shakespeare _____

2. ralph waldo emerson _____

3. louisa may alcott _____

4. richard feynman _____

5. kemal ataturk _____

6. toni morrison _____

7. felix frankfurter _____

8. thomas paine _____

9. frida kahlo _____

10. zora neal hurston _____

B. The following letter needs to be corrected. Put in the capital letters and punctuation marks. Do the work on this paper.

165 mason street

westfield il 62474

may 19, 1996

Dear rama,

i got your card yesterday i brought it to school, and we put it in the news corner

everyone wants to know more about your new home do you like your new school what is

your new bike like when are you coming back to westfield i have moved to mason street be

sure to come to see me

Your friend,

allen

Total Possible Correct: 118
(See page 104.)

IV. PAIRED DICTATION   Turn to page 119.

Lesson 21   Commas With "Yes" and "No"

I. LEARNING EXERCISE

When the word *yes* or *no* comes at the **beginning** of a sentence, it is followed by a **comma**.

Samples: *Yes, the play was very silly.*
No, I shall never be in one again.

Remember that the words *oh* and *well*, when used at the beginning of a sentence, are also followed by a comma.

Samples: *Oh, I was so embarrassed.*
Well, you know you should have taken more care.

II. PRACTICE EXERCISES

Insert commas where necessary to make the following sentences correct.

1. Yes I was in town Saturday.

2. Oh how I hate crowds!

3. No the bright lights didn't bother me.

4. No he wasn't harmed.

5. Well you should have watched where you were going.

6. Yes you may come in.

7. Yes the job is done.

8. Oh I think we may go to the museum.

9. Well what have you got there?

10. No the parade isn't until this afternoon.

III. MAINTENANCE EXERCISES

A. Place punctuation correctly in the following sentences. Underline letters that should be capitalized.

1. yes I hear you

2. please bring your skis boots wax and warm clothes

3. oh go ahead and try

4. I am ordering a camera film screen projector and case

5. they study math science and history every day

6. in our schoolroom are desks maps and chairs

7. look theresa brought two sandwiches milk an apple and some yogurt for lunch

8. will you write your name address telephone number father's name and mother's name

B. Arrange these names in alphabetical order, last name first. Watch the punctuation.

1. leonita r velez   _____

2. a myron burdick   _____

3. jasmin anderson   _____

4. matthew edwards smithson _____

5. e a hanna   _____

C. Correct the following sentences. Do the work on this paper.

1. my grandfather lives in berlin new hampshire, and i live in berlin connecticut

2. the paper i read said that rita c blasi was elected

3. wow what a mistake

Total Possible Correct: 97
(See page 105.)

IV. PAIRED DICTATION   Turn to page 119.

Lesson 22   *Commas With Conjunctions*

I. LEARNING EXERCISE

In writing stories, you may have sentences in which connecting words such as *and, or, but,* and *yet* are used. Such words are called **conjunctions**. Say the word:

con-junc-tion

These joining words, or conjunctions, can join words or phrases, or they can join two short sentences that refer to the same idea.

Samples: **Joining Words or Phrases**
1. *(Don)* **and** *(Muriel) made the tennis team.*
2. *We walked (over the hill)* **and** *(through the woods).*
3. *You may use (this chair)* **or** *(that bench).*

Joining Short Sentences
4. *Eva collected the papers,* **and** *I washed the paintbrushes.*
5. *The fire was ready to be set,* **but** *we had no matches.*

What were the conjunctions used in sentences 4 and 5? What mark of punctuation is underlined before each conjunction?

Remember this rule:
Place a **comma** (,) between two sentences that are joined with a conjunction.

II. PRACTICE EXERCISES

A. Each of the following pairs of sentences can be made into a single sentence using the conjunction given in the parentheses. Rewrite each sentence correctly in this fashion on the lines provided. Capitalize and punctuate where necessary.

(but)   1. Ted would like to play in the game. We have too many for a team already.

_____

_____

_____

(but)   2. The bell rang. We did not hear it.

_____

_____

_____

PRACTICE EXERCISES (continued)

(and)   3. I am going downtown. You are going with me.

_____

_____

_____

(or)   4. You may take your dog with you. You may stay home with him.

_____

_____

_____

(yet)   5. The colors changed. We didn't realize it.

_____

_____

_____

(and)   6. It was a cold morning. My car would not start.

_____

_____

_____

(or)   7. We may go into town. We even may go on a picnic.

_____

_____

_____

B. Read the sentences. Decide how to join these sets of sentences with the conjunctions *and*, *but*, *or*, or *yet*, and punctuate them correctly. Write the sentences on the lines provided. The first one is done for you.

1. Yvette Jones had determination. That determination helped her to win.

Yvette Jones had determination, and that determination helped her to win.

2. She ran with taped ankles. That handicap could not stop her eager spirit.

_____

_____

3. It is not always easy to overcome a handicap. It is sometimes possible to do.

_____

_____

4. You can admit failure by giving up. You can do something to change your failure into success.

_____

_____

5. He choked the carburetor. I pressed the starter button.

_____

_____

III. MAINTENANCE EXERCISES

A. Punctuate the following sentences. Do the work on this paper.

1. Yes I have seen a live penguin

2. No I haven't seen it

3. Oh I don't know

4. Well let's wait and see what the weather will be

5. Yes it is right here on the floor

6. No it is nowhere to be found

7. Oh I think we'll need crackers cheese nuts and fruit

8. Well I think the milk tastes better cold

9. Yes it is true

10. No I really don't understand

B. The following sentences need capital letters and punctuation marks. Decide where this is to be done and show the work on this paper.

1. The shortest days of the year are in the months of december january and february

2. Skating skiing and sledding are enjoyed by children in alaska

3. mae and I arranged the block-printing exhibit

MAINTENANCE EXERCISES (continued)

4. We plan to visit the friend box company watertown chamber of commerce and ideal shoe store for contributions to our fund drive

5. St patrick's day is march 17 and valentine's day is february 14

6. They went to the annual neighborhood picnic

7. Anita and i will be ready to give our mealworm report tomorrow

Total Possible Correct: 85

(See page 106.)

IV. PAIRED DICTATION   Turn to page 119.

 Lesson 23   *Commas in Appositives*

I. LEARNING EXERCISE

Read the following sentences:

1. *Goofo,* **the clown,** *will be on TV tonight.*
2. *Coach Salvi,* **a very kind man,** *retired this year.*

You will notice that in each sentence, there is a group of words that stands for another word. These are underlined. *The clown* stands for the name *Goofo.* What does *a very kind man* stand for? The groups of words *the clown* and *a very kind man* are called **appositives**. Say the word:

ap-pos-i-tive

An appositive that is made up of more than one word is set apart from the rest of the sentence by commas.

II. PRACTICE EXERCISES

In the sentences below you will find groups of words that are appositives. Remembering what you have just learned, insert the comma or commas correctly to show the appositives. Do the work right on this paper.

1. Dr. Dolittle an amazing man treated many kinds of animals.

2. His town Puddleby-on-the-Marsh was a little one.

3. His pets were Jim the shaggy dog and Too-Too the gray squirrel.

4. The lion's wife Queen Lioness liked Dr. Dolittle.

5. Robin the main character was a boy of ten.

6. Liz her sister finally won a great honor.

7. It was on Saturday that Ms. Ives the teacher took her class on a mountain-climbing trip.

8. Mr. Eagle the automobile dealer is going out of business.

9. At the science museum everyone wanted to see Black Beauty the water snake.

10. My favorite old movie *The Wizard of Oz* is on TV tonight.

III. MAINTENANCE EXERCISES

A. In the following sentences, you are to place the commas and periods where needed. Remember what you have learned about conjunctions. Do the work on this paper.

1. The gift was unwrapped and it was placed in the lobby for everyone to see

2. My tooth was aching but I did not make an appointment with the dentist

3. Helen Keller read without eyesight and she spoke without hearing

4. Students may bring their lunch or they may purchase a meal in the cafeteria

5. I arrived early today but I was still too late

B. In each exercise below are two simple, related sentences. Join them together with a conjunction and put the comma in the proper place. Use the lines provided to rewrite your sentence, capitalizing and punctuating where necessary.

1. We were all on time. Ned was not ready.

_____

_____

    2. Our friends had arrived. We were happy.

       _____

       _____

    3. We invited him. He could not come.

       _____

       _____

    4. I found Louise. Then I looked for Rebecca.

       _____

       _____

    5. Jorge was late. Sean was on time.

       _____

       _____

C. The following sentences need to be corrected. Capitalize letters and punctuate where needed. Remember what you have learned. Do your work on this paper.

    1. stop look and listen before you cross the street

    2. mother and father are away on a trip

    3. no the rodeo isn't coming to town

    4. use your eyes ears and feet

    5. yes this is the coldest winter in history

Total Possible Correct: 60
(See page 106.)

IV. PAIRED DICTATION Turn to page 119.

 **STOP**

DO NOT DO NEXT LESSON — TAKE POST TEST FIVE

Lesson 24   The Comma in Address

I. LEARNING EXERCISE

In written conversation, you may often use the name of a person as though speaking to him or her. We speak of this as "addressing the person," or using the name of a person "in direct address." Notice the different ways in which a person's name may be used "in direct address."

(at beginning)	1.	*Jeff, did you happen to see my hat? (one comma)*
(middle)	2.	*I saw it last, Mother, in your bedroom. (two commas)*
(at end)	3.	*There it is right where I left it, Son. (one comma)*

Who is **addressed** in each sentence above? *Jeff, Mother,* and *Son* are all the names of people. They are nouns that name someone addressed. Notice what mark of punctuation separates each name (noun) from the rest of the sentence. In which one of the above three sentences does the noun need two commas to separate it? Why?

Remember the rule:
When the name of a person addressed is given in a sentence, separate the name from the rest of the sentence by one or two commas depending on where the name is placed in the sentence.

II. PRACTICE EXERCISES

A. Remembering what you have learned, put commas in each of the following sentences to make them correct.

1. Barbara please find my new yarn.

2. Please be careful Roy with that chisel.

3. We can waste no time children.

4. Come here dear and sit with me.

5. What have you there Ellen that interests you so?

6. This is my new jacket Pablo.

7. Do you know how to ski Spencer?

8. No Julie there is no snow where I live.

9. Jenny do you really live in Alabama?

10. Check my skis Ginny to see if they are split.

B. Insert all marks of punctuation where needed to make the following sentences correct.

1. Don't light that flashlight Esmeralda

2. Those boys Peter are up to something

3. Yes girls how can we find our way by using the map

4. Come here Dusty

5. Here Kitty drink your milk

III. MAINTENANCE EXERCISES

A. Read the following sentences which all include appositives. Insert the correct punctuation.

1. The dog a collie belongs to Mavis.

2. Spot the spaniel belongs to the boy next door.

3. Lorraine my younger sister looks fine.

4. Mushak the little puppy was just named.

5. Sandy the puppy's mother is very protective.

6. The storm the first blizzard of the season is making big drifts.

7. Ms. González the assistant is in charge of the patrol squad.

8. Dr. Bennett our principal likes sports.

9. Suzanne Hill the captain is out sick today.

10. We waited at Terzian's the paperback store for the papers to arrive.

B. In the following list of special names of people and places, you will find the need for capital letters and punctuation. Place these corrections right on the paper.

1. new england power company

2. eli e pettigrew our director

3. capital food store

4. empire state building

5. principal ralph h doran

6. a federal courthouse

Total Possible Correct: 68

(See page 107.)

IV. PAIRED DICTATION   Turn to page 120.

Lesson 25

Direct Quotations at the Ends of Sentences

I. LEARNING EXERCISE

Writing conversation in your stories is not difficult if you follow a few simple rules. The sentences below show you the correct way to write conversation when the "who said" part (the source phrase) comes first.

Nicolas said, "Last summer my brother and I sold cold drinks."
Lucy asked, "Did you have fun?"
Nicolas exclaimed, "What a time we had!"

A direct quotation is a record of exact words spoken. The source words identify the speaker and give a clue to how the words are spoken.

Discuss together:

1. Where the comma (,) is placed.

2. Where the quotation marks (" ") come.

3. Where the period (.), question mark (?), and exclamation mark (!) are placed.

4. Which words begin with a capital letter.

Notice:

1. The comma came right after the "who said" part (Nicolas said, Lucy asked, Nicholas exclaimed).

2. The exact words of the speaker had quotation marks (" ") around them.
   a. One opening set of quotation marks is placed before the first word spoken.
   b. One closing set of quotation marks is placed after the ending punctuation of the words the speaker actually said.

3. The period, question mark, and exclamation mark came inside the quotation marks at the end of the sentence.

4. The first word of the quotation began with a capital letter because it was the beginning of a sentence or the exact words spoken.

II. PRACTICE EXERCISES

A. Proofread the following sentences of conversation. Put in the capital letters above all small letters that should be capitalized. Insert all commas, periods, question marks, exclamation marks, and quotation marks correctly where needed.

1. the prince asked whose slipper is this

2. the hen cried the sky is falling

3. the king mourned my child has turned to gold

4. the duck asked why am i so homely

5. the man shouted oh my lamp is shooting sparks

B. Write these sentences correctly on the lines provided. The first one is done for you.

1. emma suggested to jerry why don't we go into business

   Emma suggested to Jerry, "Why don't we go into business?"

2. mrs simms asked what shall we do next

3. alice quietly answered i want to keep on reading

4. jerry asked what kind of business should we try

5. emma replied with enthusiasm the computer business

6. jerry exclaimed what a thinker you are

III. MAINTENANCE EXERCISES

A. Remembering all that you have learned about capital letters and punctuation, correct the following sentences.

1. when would you care to have your first meeting mrs president

2. the new law firm is made up of three brothers: william joel and duncan

3. thank you class for giving me this honor

4. the mcCabe shoe company has moved to dallas texas

5. come anytime dr smith between 2:00 P.M. and 3:00 P.M.

6. okera your classmates have elected you

B. Correct the following short paragraph. Decide where the capital letters and punctuation belong and why they belong there. Put the corrections on the paper where needed. Remember what you have been taught.

mother frank father and i saw a parade of old automobiles this parade drove to concord providence hartford and on to new york city as they drove i heard the motors choke sputter and wheeze mayor wells of our town greeted president mercedez santana of the antique automobile association the drivers twirled the cranks jumped into the cars waved to the crowds and chugged down the road

Total Possible Correct: 136

(See page 107.)

IV. PAIRED DICTATION   Turn to page 120.

Lesson 26

Direct Quotations at the Beginnings of Sentences

I. LEARNING EXERCISE

Sometimes in written conversation, the source phrase telling "who said" will come last. Read the following. Notice where the source phrase comes.

"This town is full of junk," said Alexis.
"How can we carry it?" asked Mona.
"What an easy problem that is!" Alexis laughed.

Discuss together:
1. One opening set of quotation marks is placed before the first word spoken.
   (The closing set of quotation marks is placed after the ending punctuation of the words the speaker has actually said.)
2. A comma, rather than a period, is placed immediately after the last word spoken, except when a question mark or an exclamation mark is needed.
   (The comma, question mark, or exclamation mark is placed between the last word of the direct quotation and the closing quotation marks.)
3. A period is used after the source phrase because the quotation and source phrase together are the total sentence.
4. The first word of the direct quotation is capitalized to show that it is the first word spoken. Notice in the examples above that *said* and *asked* are not capitalized because they are not the beginnings of sentences.

II. PRACTICE EXERCISES

A. Proofread the following sentences of conversation. Insert the capital letters and punctuation as needed. Do the work on your paper.

1. we can use my cart this time said jim quickly

2. jim where can we store the junk asked jack

3. we can store it behind the garage jim told him

4. jim it will be quite a pile exclaimed jack

5. when shall we start collecting asked jim

6. jim we are going to start now stated jack

7. magazines will make us the most money offered jim

8. jim don't you think we should ask for magazines first questioned jack

9. exactly exclaimed jim

10. we're off shouted jack

B. On the lines provided rewrite the following conversation correctly. The first one is done for you.

1. our ship is now a space station stated the captain

"Our ship is now a space station," stated the captain.

2. how lonely it will be here said one of the explorers

3. will this station always be a stopping place on the way to the moon asked another astronaut

4. here is your space suit said the captain

5. quite a difference from earth weight, isn't it remarked the navigator

III. MAINTENANCE EXERCISES

A. Look at the following carefully and write three direct quotations. See your teacher for the corrections.

Captain Bell said, " _____ ."

Louis asked, " _____ ?"

Esther exclaimed, " _____ !"

B. Rewrite the following sentences correctly:

1. janet said my dog doesn't enjoy being left at home

MAINTENANCE EXERCISES (continued)

2. is there such a thing as a dog-sitter anika asked

_____

_____

3. janet answered i don't know but i've heard of dog caterers

_____

_____

4. i've heard everything chuck exclaimed

_____

_____

5. janet replied oh what will they think of next

_____

_____

C. Read the following sentences. Decide where to insert capitalization and punctuation. Remember what you have learned. Turn back and review if necessary.

1. hey look did you see the big fish captain wylie caught

2. the french boy traveled many miles looking for the visiting american soldier

3. many books tell how the pilgrims came from england

4. put the rubbish into the barrel gail

5. tom sawyer is a good book but you might like huckleberry finn better

6. some students gave reports about favorite books and others wrote reviews about them

7. mother and father were given a going-away party

8. wow this is the driest summer yet

Total Possible Correct: 156

(See page 108.)

IV. PAIRED DICTATION   Turn to page 120.

Lesson 27 　　　The Interrupted Quotation

I.　LEARNING EXERCISE

Study the following sentences carefully.

> *"The hut is getting big enough," said Setsuko, "for us to sleep in."*
> *"When," asked Gena, "can we do that?"*
> *"Girls," said her father, "what a huge hut you've built!"*

Discuss together:
1. The source phrase, or the "who said" words, divide the quotation.
2. When a source phrase interrupts, or divides, the quotation, it is set off by two commas from the words actually said.
3. One comma follows the first part of what the speaker actually said and is placed before this closing set of quotation marks. The second comma immediately follows the source phrase.
4. A period, question mark, or exclamation mark is placed between the last word of the quotation and the closing set of quotation marks.
5. The first word of the direct quotation is capitalized.
6. The first word of the second part of the direct quotation is not capitalized because it is not the first word of the quotation.

II.　PRACTICE EXERCISES

A. Insert the necessary punctuation and capitalization for the following sentences of conversation.

1. ken reminded father this lawn must be cut at once

2. please ken begged may i put it off one day longer

3. this yard replied mr chin is a mess and a disgrace

4. well asked ken is this all my job

5. son demanded mr chin you had better make it your business

B. Correct the following sentences with capital letters and punctuation where necessary.

1. once said ruth we were all away

2. then asked teresa did your aunt come to the house

3. she came ruth laughed and waited for one call

4. when the phone rang asked teresa what did she do

5. she lifted the receiver ruth said and she sounded disappointed

III. MAINTENANCE EXERCISES

A. Insert the necessary punctuation and capitalization for the following sentences of conversation. Do the work on this paper.

1. may i put air in my bicycle tires asked karin

2. help yourself the attendant said but wind the air hose when you're through

3. karin asked is it hard to work in a gas station

4. only when we have five or six customers at one time answered the attendant

5. well thank you for your favor responded karin

B. Remembering what you have learned about capital letters, punctuation, and titles of books, correct the following book list. Check with Lesson 19 first if you need to.

brink carol r	baby island
emily douglas r	appleseed farm
field rachel l	taxis and toadstools
perkins lucy f	the dutch twins

C. Correct the following sentences with capital letters and punctuation where necessary. Do the work right on this paper.

1. the wilderness club is meeting in the mirror lake hotel this afternoon

2. the greensboro community chorus is giving a concert on sunday march 14, at 1:45 P.M.

3. the shelton chamber of commerce is located in the center of town

spring fever

i have spring fever as anyone can see;

it really has a grip on me!

whenever i can, i slump in a chair;

my feet are just the laziest pair.

Total Possible Correct: 188

(See page 109.)

IV. PAIRED DICTATION Turn to page 120.

Lesson 28   The Indirect Quotation

I. LEARNING EXERCISE

In an indirect quotation, ideas are written that have been expressed by someone. The exact words expressing that idea are now written, so quotation marks are not used.

> Samples:
> Direct quotation: *Tim said, "My gas-engine plane is stuck in the tree."*
> Indirect quotation: *Tim said that his gas-engine plane was stuck in the tree.*
>
> *Tim told me that his gas-engine plane was stuck in the tree.*

Notice:
No separating punctuation marks are used between the source of the idea (Tim) and his idea in the indirect quotations. A slight change or addition of words may be needed to change a direct quotation into an indirect quotation.

Discussion:
1. Quotation marks enclose the exact words spoken.
2. The first word of each sentence in a quotation begins with a capital.
3. The period, question mark, or exclamation mark is placed between the last word of the quotation and the closing set of quotation marks.
4. When the quotation comes first, a comma is placed before the source phrase and the closing set of quotation marks.
5. When the quotation comes last, the source phrase is followed by a comma.
6. In conversations, source phrases are sometimes understood and not used.

II. PRACTICE EXERCISES

A. Correct the following sentences on this paper. Use all punctuation and capitalization necessary.

1. deena told her little brother to go home

2. go home andy said deena

3. she explained to cecila that her brother always followed her

4. i have a brother just like him answered cecila

5. i guess we can agree that little brothers get in the way

6. deena remembered that little brothers are sometimes nice to have around on rainy days

7. cecila remarked that her brother was always willing to share

8. the girls then agreed that little brothers weren't so bad after all

PRACTICE EXERCISES (continued)

B. Rewrite the following sentences. Remember your rules for punctuation and capitalization. Write the sentence given as (a) a direct quotation and (b) an indirect quotation. You may change or add words in writing.

1. debbie said jump over the bush

    a. _____

    b. _____

2. nina replied that she didn't want to because she was wearing new pants

    a. _____

    b. _____

3. then watch me suggested debbie as i do it

    a. _____

    b. _____

4. nina agreed that it was a pretty good trick

    a. _____

    b. _____

III. MAINTENANCE EXERCISES

A. Correct the following sentences. Remember all you have learned about capitalization and punctuation.

1. come on over julio and help me with the bike suggested carlos

2. julio complained that he had to buy some new shoes that day

3. then julio remembered that it was because carlos had borrowed the bike that it was no

    longer working

4. when you lent it to me reminded carlos i showed you where the chain was loose

5. my uncle eduardo salas at the maple street garage will help you

6. is that the garage julio between elm street and park place

MAINTENANCE EXERCISES (continued)

B. Correct the following sentences. Remember all you have learned about capitalization and punctuation.

1. sylvester speer my sister's husband will be visiting us on monday tuesday wednesday and thursday

2. did father read mutiny on the bounty by nordhoff and hall

3. selectman george e moore cut the ribbon at the opening of f h lily company

4. the orlando boosters club is sponsoring the colts this year said miles

5. will you do it now sally or do you want to wait until after the meeting asked mother

Total Possible Correct: 158
(See page 109.)

IV. **PAIRED DICTATION**   Turn to page 121.

Lesson 29   *Writing Conversation*

I. LEARNING EXERCISE

In written conversation, a new paragraph begins with each change of speaker.

A paragraph tells about one topic. It **may** be made up of one sentence or a group of sentences. The first word of each paragraph is always indented. Notice how the following is written:

Ronny explained to the veterinarian that his dog was not feeling well.

The veterinarian said to Ronny, "Your dog must take a tablespoonful of this medicine twice each day."

"How can Dewdrop do that? He drinks out of a pan," Ronny told the vet. "How am I to get him to swallow it?"

"Just mix it in with his water."

Notice:
The first paragraph is an indirect quotation, but still requires a paragraph of its own.

II. PRACTICE EXERCISES

A. Rewrite the following story, remembering all you have learned about written conversation.

i went fishing yesterday henry said jean asked did you catch anything i caught a fish so big that i could not get it into the boat it finally pulled me overboard said henry jean asked if he got wet no laughed henry i landed on its back

_____

_____

_____

_____

_____

_____

_____

_____

_____

B. Rewrite the following story, remembering all you have learned about written conversation.

how will you ever get that huge melon down to the river asked al tania answered my sixty oxen can haul it down but you don't have a raft that is big enough said al i'll build one shouted tania or maybe i'll float it down in one of my sister's wooden shoes

_____

_____

_____

_____

_____

_____

_____

_____

_____

III. MAINTENANCE EXERCISES

A. Correct the following sentences of conversation on this paper. Remember what you have learned.

1. the road conditions are so bad remarked andre that we won't drive

2. oh said walter is it really that bad outside

3. yes he replied cars are slipping all over the road

4. in that case added walter it would be wise to remain at home

5. the weather sounds better for tomorrow said andre so that now we will be able to travel

   after all

B. Correct the following sentences with capital letters and punctuation marks where needed.

1. we'll invite martha and marita the twins from across the street

2. mother said yes you may have to help father unload the car

3. the american heart association has a fund drive in february

4. we can buy our tools at lang's supply suggested the scout leader

5. hooray we'll start writing invitations now

Total Possible Correct: 145

(See page 110.)

IV. PAIRED DICTATION   Turn to page 121.

STOP
DO NOT DO NEXT LESSON — TAKE POST TEST SIX

Lesson 30   The Apostrophe in Contractions

I. LEARNING EXERCISE

Repeat these two words: con-trac-tion   a-pos-tro-phe

A **contraction** is one word that has been made from two.
Samples: *can't (can not)*
don't (do not)
isn't (is not)

In contractions, an apostrophe (') is put in the word to show you that a letter or letters have been left out. The words *am, is, are, have, will,* and *would* are often combined with words to make contractions.

Samples: *I'm (I **am**)*   *they've (they **have**)*
*we're (we **are**)*   *we'll (we **will**)*
*it's (it **is**)*   *she'd (she **would**)*
Exception: *won't (**will not**)*

II. PRACTICE EXERCISES

A. Using what you have learned above, write the contraction that belongs in the blanks in the sentences below. The words you are to make contractions from are before the sentence.

can not   1. I _____ go to the library today.

Do not   2. _____ touch the poison ivy.

are not   3. Some children _____ able to play in the game.

will not   4. Did you say you _____ be up early tomorrow?

was not   5. Austin _____ asked if he enjoyed the movie.

I will   6. _____ soon be old enough to drive.

had not   7. Joe _____ touched the baby woodchucks.

are not   8. There _____ any pencils left.

did not   9. The visitors _____ find any trail to the mountaintop.

Who is   10. Mother asked, "_____ planning to be with you at the beach?"

she would   11. Jarilyn assured her mother that _____ be back in time for lunch.

We will   12. _____ promise to help you when you need it.

has not   13. Laura _____ packed her bag for the vacation trip.

That is   14. _____ the best model on display.

Let us   15. _____ watch the movies on TV tonight.

B. Read the contractions below. For which words does each contraction stand? Write the words on the line after each contraction.

1. doesn't   _____   8. they've   _____

2. they're   _____   9. we're   _____

3. you've   _____   10. he's   _____

4. he'll   _____   11. hadn't   _____

5. you'll   _____   12. weren't   _____

6. couldn't   _____   13. I'm   _____

7. it's   _____   14. she's   _____

III. MAINTENANCE EXERCISES

A. Capitalize and punctuate the following short conversation on this paper. Remember all your rules for conversation.

that police officer said fred took my new ball bat and glove how did that happen asked dr

carter my friends and i were playing ball here in the street replied fred didn't he give a

reason asked dr carter well yes answered fred he had told us before that playing ball in the

street is against the law this time he took away my ball bat and glove

_____

_____

_____

_____

_____

_____

_____

_____

_____

MAINTENANCE EXERCISES (continued)

B. Capitalize the following list of items correctly. Put the capital letter above the small letter to be capitalized. Insert periods where needed.

dr laski   representative maceda   a stamp club

a j wolsky   pres wanda butman   boy scouts of america

C. Insert the punctuation only where needed to correct the sentence.

1. Representatives from the United States China Japan and France attended the meeting

2. Volcanoes lakes waterfalls and mountains make the scenery of Alaska beautiful

3. Hurry and get ready for bed called Mother

4. The children replied we are already in bed

Total Possible Correct: 117

(See page 111.)

IV. PAIRED DICTATION   Turn to page 121.

Lesson 31

The Apostrophe in Singular Possessives

I. LEARNING EXERCISE

Sometimes you need to use nouns that show who owns the object you are talking about, or what it is a part of. Notice the underlined words below. They each speak of a singular person or animal (one girl, one woodchuck, etc). These underlined nouns tell who owns the thing or things we are talking about.

the **girl's** books   **Rena's** coat
Gloria's pens   **Chris's** arm
the **woodchuck's** tail   a **knight's** armor

What mark of punctuation is used in the underlined words? You can see an *'s* (apostrophe and *s*) is added to each noun to make it show possession. The underlined nouns are called **singular possessives**. An *'s* (apostrophe and *s*) is added to a singular noun to make it show possession.

II. PRACTICE EXERCISES

A. In the sentences below, underline each word that shows possession.

1. Arthur's brother is older than he is.

2. The man's grandfather was a pioneer.

3. This boy's home was in Nebraska.

4. The beaver's lodge was destroyed in the flood.

5. The oldest sister's name was Nancy.

6. The computer's keyboard was jammed.

7. An Indian woman came to visit Roma's mother.

8. The space shuttle's mission lasted three weeks.

9. The audience applauded the choir's performance.

10. Sasha enjoyed the woman's company.

B. In each sentence below, write on the blank line the possessive form of the word in parentheses. The first one is done for you.

1. I hear the _____*boy's*_____ voice. (boy)

2. _____ brother lives in Los Angeles. (Consuelo)

3. The _____ home is in the tree trunk. (squirrel)

4. He borrowed _____ baseball bat. (Ross)

5. Do you know _____ mother? (Claire)

6. _____ name is not on the list. (Mrs. Tsung)

7. It was the _____ points that won the game. (captain)

8. The _____ hose did not reach the flame. (fire fighter)

9. Have you ever played table tennis at _____ house? (Helena)

10. What a lot of paint in that _____ hair! (girl)

III. MAINTENANCE EXERCISES

A. On the space provided for each sentence rewrite the underlined words as contractions. Put punctuation in each sentence if needed.

1. **It is** time for you to get up Alex **is** it **not**?   _____   _____

2. Paul knows his lesson well, **does** he **not**?   _____

3. Mother said "I **would not** let you do it."   _____

4. Nathan you **have not** done your work very well.   _____

5. Juana **we are** going to go with you.   _____

6. **Does** it **not** rain very hard?   _____

7. **They are** late **are** they **not**?   _____   _____

8. **Was** Kristen **not** younger than Rene?   _____

9. We **will not** be riding with you Curtis.   _____

10. **Could** you **not** come home from the park early?   _____

B. On the lines provided write what is asked for. Capitalize and punctuate correctly.

1. An interrogative sentence:

_____

_____

2. An exclamatory sentence:

_____

_____

3. The name of:

a shoe store: _____

a milk company: _____

a factory: _____

a city and state: _____

C. Put the punctuation where needed in the following sentences.

1. Yes we have no bananas

2. When for heavens sake did you do that

3. Axel begged please may I go to the movies on Saturday

4. I have said no for the last time replied Mother

5. If I do all my chores at home and school added Axel then will you let me go

Total Possible Correct: 65

(See page 111.)

IV. **PAIRED DICTATION**   Turn to page 121.

Lesson 32

The Apostrophe in Plural Possessives

I. LEARNING EXERCISE

A noun that names more than one is a plural noun. When a plural noun ends in *s*, only an apostrophe (') is added to make it show possession.

Samples: ***boys'*** *hats*
        girls' *shoes*

When a plural noun does not end in *s*, an *'s* is added to make it show possession.

Samples: ***men's*** *handkerchiefs*
        women's *stockings*
        children's *books*

The underlined nouns are called **plural possessives**.

II. PRACTICE EXERCISES

A. Read the sentences below and write in the blank the possessive form of the word in parentheses.

1. I know those _____ names. (boys)

2. The _____ campout is tonight. (girls)

3. The _____ jamboree was held last week. (scouts)

4. The _____ heirlooms are worth money. (Joneses)

5. The _____ manes are bushy. (ponies)

6. The sound of the _____ hooves echoed in the valley. (horses)

7. Mother went out to the sale of _____ dresses. (women)

8. Have you ever noticed the _____ paths in the sky? (stars)

9. _____ stories always sound so interesting. (Children)

B. In the following sentences, write on the blank line the possessive form of the word in parentheses.

1. The _____ show was a huge success. (children)

2. The _____ food was all gone. (mice)

3. I saw the two _____ antlers were just beginning to grow. (deer)

4. The _____ feathers shed water. (geese)

5. We saw the _____ swimming classes. (beginners)

6. The _____ skating group won first place. (women)

7. The _____ coats were hanging out to dry. (fire fighters)

8. All of the _____ efforts were lost in the rescue. (police officers)

III. MAINTENANCE EXERCISES

A. Read the following sentences. Decide if the word in parentheses is singular or plural. Write the correct form of the word.

1. _____ dog is a collie. (Alfred)

2. That spaniel belongs to the _____ next door. (boys)

3. The _____ spaniel belongs with them. (boys)

4. The _____ name is Mike. (puppy)

5. His _____ dog is a terrier. (aunt)

6. The _____ mother is now gone. (dog)

7. I could faintly hear the _____ voice. (announcer)

8. The _____ plow broke in the storm. (truck)

9. Our _____ cat is missing. (neighbor)

10. The _____ pumpers worked all night. (fire fighters)

B. Decide which two words make up the contractions below and write them on the line provided.

it'll	_____	won't	_____
I'm	_____	we'll	_____
wouldn't	_____	you'll	_____
shouldn't	_____	we've	_____

C. Underline the letters that need to be made capital letters and insert the punctuation only where necessary.

1. **Titles of reports:**

   parts of an airplane   in the control tower

   watching the weather   a trip in a jet

2. Our new home on pine tree road was bought by mother and father

3. The english french and dutch were among the first settlers in america

4. the list contains the following names:

       amato victor p   ector a h

       montez blanca r   hayes e cicely

5. a dogs leash was found after being lost five days

6. dougs mother is working in her office

7. the childrens department was crowded

D. Punctuate the following excerpt from a familiar story.

i dont see how you can stand such poor food all the time the town mouse said to his country cousin why dont you come home with me

i should be glad to said the country mouse

at first the country mouse enjoyed his cousins fine food this is wonderful said the country mouse i shall stay here forever

just then a huge cat appeared frightened half out of their wits the two mice ran for shelter

Total Possible Correct: 130

(See page 112.)

IV. PAIRED DICTATION   Turn to page 122.

STOP   **DO NOT DO NEXT LESSON — TAKE POST TEST SEVEN**

Lesson 33
Capitalizing Geographical Terms (Rivers, Oceans, Mountains, and Continents)

I. LEARNING EXERCISE

Geographical terms naming a specific place require capital letters. Use a **capital letter** to begin such terms as those that name **rivers**, **oceans**, **mountains**, etc.

Samples: *Ohio River, Arctic Ocean, Green Mountains*

It is also necessary to use a **capital letter** to begin words that name continents.

Samples: *Australia*
          North America

When geographical terms are used as adjectives, or descriptive words, they should be capitalized.

Samples: *North American Continent, Ohio River Delta*

II. PRACTICE EXERCISES

A. Underline the letters that should begin with a capital letter.

1. white mountains	7. a short creek	13. adirondack mountains
2. ashley river	8. europe	14. a tall mountain
3. aegean sea	9. a narrow stream	15. atlantic ocean
4. charles river	10. south america	16. ohio river
5. a continent	11. down the river	17. pikes peak
6. a meandering brook	12. asia	18. africa

B. Some of the capital letters and punctuation are missing in the following paragraph. Underline the letters that should be capitalized. Punctuate the paragraph.

were told paper was first made by people in asia many years ago. Its said the egyptians made it from a reed that grew along the nile river. the chinese, however, were really the first to make paper. today some of the finest paper is made in europe. this paper is shipped across the atlantic ocean to the united states. its then sent to all points west, crossing the mississippi river and the rocky mountains.

III. MAINTENANCE EXERCISES

A. On the lines provided write the possessive form of the word in parentheses. The first one is done for you.

1. At (John Hancock) suggestion the colonies planned to unite.

   John Hancock's

2. British soldiers searched the (citizens) houses for smuggled goods.

   _____

3. The (redcoats) orders were to raid the supplies of the minutemen.

   _____

4. The minutemen assembled at the (messenger) warning.

   _____

5. The battle that followed led to the (general) retreat.

   _____

6. The (soldiers) bravery was outstanding.

   _____

B. Certain words in the following list of names, events, countries, etc., need capital letters. Decide which words need to begin with a capital letter and underline the letter to be changed.

1. memorial day

2. the 19th of april

3. vietnamese

4. sri lanka

5. thursday night

6. ms lucia m rivera

C. Insert commas and apostrophes to correct the following sentences.

1. Our new cookbook tells how to make soups salads casseroles and bread.

2. The boys uncle came to visit him.

3. Its time for you to get up angela isn't it?

Total Possible Correct: 68
(See page 113.)

IV. PAIRED DICTATION   Turn to page 122.

Lesson 34 · Capitalizing Geographical Terms (Regions and Sections)

I. LEARNING EXERCISE

Another use for the capital letter is with names of regions or sections of a country. **Do not** use a capital letter for words that give a compass direction or for words that are **not** the formal name of an area.

Samples: *We settled in the **East**. (region)*
*Are you traveling **west**? (compass direction)*
*We lived in **western** Michigan (description, not formal name of area)*

Notice that in the first sentence, an area of the country is named, so a capital letter is used. In the second sentence, a direction of travel is mentioned, and this use of the word does **not** require a capital letter. In the third sentence, the word *western* describes Michigan and does **not** require a capital letter.

II. PRACTICE EXERCISES

A. Underline the letters that should begin with a capital letter.

1. winds moving north
2. western connecticut
3. driving out west
4. northern lights
5. clouds hastening south

6. turn west
7. eastern section
8. face east
9. north dakota
10. northeastern

11. sailing west
12. in the north
13. flying to the south
14. west indies
15. eastward flight

B. Put capital letters above the words where needed in the following sentences.

1. much cotton is grown in the south.

2. in winter the birds fly south.

3. sugar beets are raised in the west and in the southwest.

4. winters are milder in the southern part of our country.

5. the western sky abruptly filled with rain clouds.

III. MAINTENANCE EXERCISES

A. Remembering what you have learned, capitalize the following sentences correctly. Put a capital letter above the letter needing to be capitalized.

1. the colorado river flows through arizona and new mexico.

2. the tallest mountain in the united states is mount mcKinley.

3. have you ever seen the redson river in the northern part of our state?

4. much salmon is caught in puget sound, in the state of washington.

5. the suez canal joins the red sea with the mediterranean.

B. In the following exercises you are asked to write some information. Remember what you have learned about capital letters and write the information correctly.

1. What is the name of your town library? _____

2. What school do you attend? _____

3. Name one bank in town. _____

4. Write the name of a club in town. _____

C. Use quotation marks and capital letters in the following sentences where necessary.

1. She said, I can't let you do it.

2. I have a book for you, said the teacher.

3. Henry Clay said that he would rather be right than president.

4. Where are you going pleaded andrea that I can't go with you?

Total Possible Correct: 59
(See page 113.)

IV. PAIRED DICTATION   Turn to page 122.

Lesson 35   The Colon

I. LEARNING EXERCISE

Here are two uses for the colon.

Samples: 1. *The school building is opened at 8:15 A.M. each day.*

2. *Please send the following: stamps, a box top, a label, and a written story.*

Sentence 1 shows you how to use the **colon** (:) when writing hours and minutes. The **colon** (:) always **separates** the number for the hours from the number for the minutes.

Sentence 2 indicates how the colon (:) is used in writing when introducing a number of **items** or **ideas** in a list.

II. PRACTICE EXERCISES

A. Here are five clock faces. Write the time told by each clock under each clock face.

_____   _____   _____   _____   _____

B. Write the following times correctly in numbers: The first one is done for you.

1. twelve forty in the afternoon   _____

2. eight thirty in the evening   _____

3. two o'clock in the morning   _____

4. quarter past six in the evening   _____

5. quarter of eight in the morning   _____

PRACTICE EXERCISES (continued)

C. Put a colon in the following sentences where needed. Make other necessary changes or additions to correct these sentences.

1. The trains stop in new york at these times 820 am 1200 noon and 320 pm

2. Please send me one copy of each of these books famous women historical heroes and book of myths

3. Get these things for me at the store bread milk cheese and eggs

4. The early bus leaves at 145 pm and the later bus leaves at 230 pm

5. School is usually dismissed at 305 pm

III. MAINTENANCE EXERCISES

Correct the following sentences.

1. the first movie theater opened on april 2 1902, in los angeles

2. dad will you teach me to golf begged olivia

3. mrs carr the fifth-grade teacher suggested that we use watercolors

4. oh eric marilyn called from the kitchen help me my soup is boiling over

5. denise the canadian girl in our class speaks french

6. on june 1 1954, congress changed the name armistice day to veterans day

7. do you prefer to live in the east or the west

8. dr a j djar of the minnesota department of wildlife will speak to us next monday at 930 am on the need for conservation

9. hilda is reading the giving tree and i have nearly finished treasure island remarked matt

10. dr audrey chapman-steele directed a number of expeditions to eastern africa for the american museum of natural history

Total Possible Correct: 169

(See page 114.)

IV. PAIRED DICTATION Turn to page 122.

TAKE POST TEST EIGHT

ANSWERS

Lesson 1: STATEMENTS AND COMMANDS

II. PRACTICE EXERCISES

A. 2. **We** . . . together.
    3. **The** . . . fair.
    4. **Sit** . . . seat.

    5. **The** . . . home.
    6. **The** . . . over.
    7. **Telephone** . . . late.

    8. **Run** . . . field.
    9. **The** . . . feet.
    10. **Get** . . . early.

B. **One** . . . bicycle. **It** . . . day. **Suddenly** . . . curb. **She** . . . trouble. **Quickly** . . . glass. **She** . . . glass. **Maria** . . . day.

Lesson 2: QUESTIONS AND EXCLAMATIONS

II. PRACTICE EXERCISES

2. **Do** . . . partner?
3. **A** . . . yard!
4. **Are** . . . game?

5. **What** . . . is!
6. **Did** . . . chalkboard?
7. **What** . . . do?

8. **Look** out!
9. **Help!**
10. **Someone** . . . now!

III. MAINTENANCE EXERCISES

1. **What** . . . her?
2. **At** . . . sure.
3. **How** horrible!
4. **Was** . . . there?
5. **The** . . . announcement.

6. **The** . . . auditorium.
7. **My** . . . group.
8. **She** . . . watching.
9. **Be** . . . help!
10. **My** . . . loudly.

11. **She** . . . her!
12. **They** . . . immediately.
13. **Answer** . . . question.
14. **Did** . . . there?

Lesson 3: THE INTERJECTION

II. PRACTICE EXERCISES

1. **Hurrah! We** . . . ready.
2. **Great! They're** . . . last.
3. **Oh,** . . . bat.
4. **Look! It's** . . . you.
5. **My,** . . . quiet.

6. **Well,** . . . it.
7. **Yes,** . . . you.
8. **Congratulations! You** won.
9. **Hurray! The** . . . over.
10. **Ouch! These** . . . hurt.

III. MAINTENANCE EXERCISES

A. 1. **When** . . . ready?
    2. **Sit** . . . canoe.
    3. **The** . . . tomorrow.
    4. **Look** . . . rocket!
    5. **I** . . . market.

    6. **What** . . . had!
    7. **Did** . . . Venus?
    8. **We** . . . yesterday.
    9. **Oh,** . . . fun.
    10. **Another** . . . high.

B. **We** . . . week. **It** . . . family. **We** . . . before. **The** . . . sounds. **The** . . . orders. **We** . . . sleep. **Do** . . . did? **As** . . . sleep. **We** . . . fair.

Lesson 4: ABBREVIATIONS

II. PRACTICE EXERCISES

A. 1. **M**rs. Rosa Ciani
   2. 16 in.
   3. **M**r. Calvin Washington
   4. **P**res. Abraham Lincoln
   5. 24 Woodward **A**ve. or 5 Lee **S**t.
   6. **M**on. or **F**ri. or **S**at.

B. 2. **T**ues. . . . Tuesday
   3. lb . . . pound
   4. no. . . . number
   5. **A**ve. . . . Avenue
   6. **M**r. . . . Mister
   7. **D**r. . . . Doctor

8. **S**ept. . . . September
9. ft . . . foot or feet
10. **R**d. . . . Road

III. MAINTENANCE EXERCISES

<u>N</u>ick . . . house. <u>H</u>e . . . ready. <u>N</u>ick's . . . stove. <u>I</u>t . . . library. <u>N</u>ick's . . . weeks. <u>H</u>e . . . it. <u>W</u>hat luck! <u>T</u>hey . . . way. <u>T</u>he . . . six. <u>N</u>ick . . . locked. <u>W</u>hat . . . fate? <u>H</u>e . . . wanted. <u>H</u>ave . . . one?

Lesson 5: CAPITALIZING NAMES AND INITIALS

II. PRACTICE EXERCISES

1. **E**ileen **N**ovak . . . speech.
2. **A** . . . **K**arl . . . school.
3. **M**s. **L**evy . . . party.
4. **W**hat . . . **L**eroy led.
5. **Y**esterday **J**ane **E**astman . . . paper.

6. **I**t . . . **O**lga and **E**lena . . . week.
7. **C**hiang's . . . chalkboard.
8. **D**id **Y**vonne . . . **N**ibs?
9. **T**he . . . **M**r. **S**an **M**iguel.

III. MAINTENANCE EXERCISES

A. 1. **F**ather . . . **M**s. **A. J. B**auer.
   2. **T**he . . . gift.
   3. **I**n . . . party.

4. **T**om . . . **M**rs. **N**ora **C. R**iley.
5. **D**r. **J. R. P**appas . . . accident.
6. **W**e . . . game.

B. **L**ast . . . country. **O**n . . . **M**r. **B**oudreau. **M**other . . . magazine. **M**other . . . him. **H**e . . . home. **I** . . . more. **D**r. **B**rown . . . me. **I** . . . away. **D**r. **B**rown . . . me.

Lesson 6: TITLES BELONGING TO PEOPLE

II. PRACTICE EXERCISES

1. **T**he . . . **D**r. **R**usso . . . Hospital.
2. **A** . . . **S**enator **E**ckstein or **R**epresentative **J**ohnson.
3. **A**re . . . **T**reasurer **C**alhoun today?
4. **H**as **P**resident **S**chmidt . . . law?
5. **G**eneral **B**roadbent . . . parade.

III. MAINTENANCE EXERCISES

A. **S**un., **M**on., **T**ues., **W**ed., **T**hurs., **F**ri., **S**at.

B. **J**an., **F**eb., **M**ar., **A**pr.,
   Aug., **S**ept., **O**ct., **N**ov., **D**ec.

C. **I**t . . . April 1. **M**y . . . deli.
   We . . . sandwiches. **W**hen . . . cent.
   This . . . joke. **H**e . . . **O**h no! **Y**ou . . . have."
   As . . . money. **H**ave . . . this?

II. PRACTICE EXERCISES

Note that your underlined titles appear in italics in the answers.

A. 1. *Across America on an Emigrant Train* by Jim Murphy
    2. *The Wind in the Willows* by Kenneth Grahame
    3. *The Hubble Space Telescope* by Gregory Vogt
    4. *The Pelican Chorus* by Edward Lear
    5. *Missing May* by Cynthia Rylant
    6. *The Summer of the Swans* by Betsy Byar
    7. *Charlotte's Web* by E. B. White
    8. *A String in the Harp* by Nancy Bond

B. 1. Jill . . . *Harriet Tubman* . . . report.
    2. The . . . *Johnny Tremain* by Esther Forbes.
    3. The . . . "Exploration of Mars" . . . library.
    4. Our . . . "Together" . . . *America*.
    5. My . . . "A Dream Deferred" by Langston Hughes, . . . *Youth*.
    6. Is . . . "Scenes of Summer" . . . *Herald Recorder* ?
    7. Please . . . "Home on the Range" in *Music for Young Singers*.

III. MAINTENANCE EXERCISES

A. 1. Mr. Arnold E. Banelow
    2. Dr. Esther B. Levine
    3. 15 East Clark St.
    4. 884 Fenton Ave.

    5. Sen. Cecilia Sanchez
    6. Gen. Dexter Carlton
    7. Dec. 1999
    8. Gov. Oliver Winslow

B. It . . . Sunday. Dr. Casey . . . driveway. I . . . fast. My . . . Capt. Horace Williams . . . her. I . . . help. We . . . Dr. Casey . . . hospital. An . . . help. What . . . caused!

Lesson 8: CAPITALIZING FIRST WORD
OF EVERY LINE OF POETRY

II. PRACTICE EXERCISES

A. Jonathan Gee

Jonathan Gee
Struck at a bee;
A sadder and wiser
Boy is he.

He's nursing a sting
That burns like fire,
And has put his beehive
Out for hire.

Looking Up

Jonathan Gee
Has troubles to spare;
He walks, you see,
With his nose in the air.

Jonathan Gee
With his mind in a muddle
Watched a bud in a tree
And fell into a puddle.

B. **A Limerick**

There . . .
Who . . .
  But . . .
  He . . .
And . . .

III. MAINTENANCE EXERCISES

A. 1. "A Talking Hound"
  2. An Army of Fleas
  3. "Time on My Hands"
  4. "The Umbrella by the Door"
  5. Doctor Dolittle's Zoo
  6. "A Lesson for Andy"
  7. High Flight
  8. "Winter Song"

B. 1. Oh, . . .
  2. Hurray! Our . . .
  3. Wait, . . .
  4. Oh! . . .
  5. Ouch! . . .
  6. Horrors! Did . . .

Lesson 9: CAPITALIZING FATHER AND MOTHER

II. PRACTICE EXERCISES

Dear Grandmother,
  Thank . . . you. Both Mother and Father . . . go. May . . . June? My . . . train. I will . . . 2:30. How . . . Grandfather! Mother and Father . . . everyone.

III. MAINTENANCE EXERCISES

A. First Star

Star . . .
  First . . .
  . . .
  Have . . .

The Butterfly

Up . . .
Like . . .
  . . .
Gliding . . .

B. 1. Are . . . *Sounder* . . . report?
  2. He . . . ice!
  3. We . . . *Danger Is My Business* by H. Craig.
  4. Aren't . . . line?
  5. Ow! You're . . . me!
  6. Do . . . easy?
  7. The . . . "Graphing Data" . . . mathematicians.

Lesson 10: CAPITALIZING "I"

II. PRACTICE EXERCISES

1. Last . . . I . . .
2. I . . . I . . .
3. My . . . "When I Was . . . Hospital."

4. The . . . I . . . Frisky.
5. I . . .
6. I . . . Ms. Yumi Numata.

III. MAINTENANCE EXERCISES

1. It . . . Columbus.
2. Sit . . . down.
3. Mother and Father . . . birthday.
4. Do . . . Street . . . Avenue?
5. My . . . Father . . . skiing.
6. Have . . . please.
7. I . . . Father and Mother . . . town.
8. We . . . later.

Lesson 11: CAPITALIZING NAMES OF COMPANIES AND STORES

II. PRACTICE EXERCISES

A. 1–10 One point for each correctly written name.
Ask your teacher to check this exercise for you.

B.
1. The United Shoe Company . . . area.
2. When . . . I . . . Shopper's Warehouse.
3. I . . . Lazeon Corporation.
4. She . . . Martinez Advertising Agency . . . retired.
5. Did . . . Catalina's . . . Boston?
6. I . . . Canadian National Railway . . . report.
7. My . . . Charleston Electric Light Company.

III. MAINTENANCE EXERCISES

A.
1. The . . . J.F.K. . . . President John Fitzgerald Kennedy.
2. The . . . United States . . . Dwight D. Eisenhower.
3. I . . . Ms. Carla L. Almeida.
4. Coach Folger . . . Principal Schmidt . . . practice.
5. Lihwa Chang, Shelton Little, Shani Marks, Howard Davis, and I . . . team.
6. Mary Lou and I . . . tonight.
7. Dr. Scott . . . I . . . chart.
8. I . . . *Black Stallion.*

B.
1. I . . . I . . . Explorers.
2. Give . . . father.
3. Yea! We . . . championship.
4. The . . . "Never the Winner" . . . Elaine Meyer.
5. She . . . I . . . *Tribune.*
6. His . . . *Sports World.*
7. Well, . . . results.
8. Officer Tracey . . . Clarkson Cleaners.

Lesson 12: CAPITALIZING NAMES OF BUILDINGS AND SPECIAL PLACES

II. PRACTICE EXERCISES

A. 1–5 One point for each correctly written name.

B.
1. Seattle Chamber of Commerce
2. The White House
3. Tulane University
4. Fairmont Park
5. no capitals
6. Morgan Country Day School
7. Bates College
8. Yellowstone National Park
9. Library of Congress
10. no capital

A. 1. Finnegan's Book Store
   2. Suki Onuki, Mgr., Stop and Spend Co.
   3. Mulligan's . . . New York.
   4. My . . . Mears, E.M.T. Schelf, and Priceless . . . job.
   5. The . . . report.
   6. The Whim-Wham Company . . . Atlanta.

B. Dear Indira,

We . . . Captain Bill's . . . boat. I . . . thing. The . . . Mrs. Consuelo T. Diaz . . . fish. It . . . I . . . saw. Before . . . swim. What . . . had! I . . . soon. We . . . together.
                                  Anna M. Weiss

Lesson 13: CAPITALIZING NAMES OF CLUBS AND SPECIAL GROUPS

II. PRACTICE EXERCISES

A. 1. The . . . Cub Scouts . . .
   2. The Johnstown Garden Club . . .
   3. We . . . Ashmont Achievement Association
   4. The Little League Browns . . .
   5. The Cincinnati Nurses' Aides Association . . .
   6. The Braxton Athletic League . . .
   7. Would . . . Richmond Stadium Authority?
   8. A United States Coast Guard . . .

B. 1. Fri.
   2. no capitals
   3. the Chagrin Falls Glee Club
   4. the Atlanta Archery Team
   5. the C. E. Society
   6. no capitals
   7. the American Heart and Lung Association
   8. White Sox
   9. no capitals

III. MAINTENANCE EXERCISES

A. 2–11 One point for each correctly written name.
Ask your teacher to check your list.

B. "A Crazy Halloween Party"
"Headlights and Taillights"
"Colonial Furniture"
"America's First President"
"From Tadpoles to Frogs"

C. The Cobbler

Crooked heels
And scuffy toes
Are all the kinds
Of shoes he knows.

He patches up
The broken places,
Sews the seams,
And shines their faces.

          E. A. Chaffee

Lesson 14: CAPITALIZING NAMES OF DAYS, SPECIAL DAYS, AND HOLIDAYS

II. PRACTICE EXERCISES

1. We . . . Thanksgiving.
2. Martin Luther King Day and New Year's Day . . . month.
3. It . . . Sunday . . . April.
4. They . . . Fourth of July rocket.
5. San Jacinto Day and Kuhio Day . . . states.
6. We . . . Memorial Day play.
7. I . . . Veterans Day parade.
8. School . . . Labor Day.

III. MAINTENANCE EXERCISES

A.
1. 4-H Club
2. Norfolk Bay United Fund
3. National Education Association
4. White Sox
5. no capitals
6. no capitals
7. E. A. Haskell Foundation
8. Midwestern Running Association
9. no capitals
10. M. M. King School Safety Patrol

B. Luther Burbank . . . scientist. He . . . plants. He . . . fruits. He . . . farms.

Lesson 15: CAPITALIZING NAMES OF STREETS

II. PRACTICE EXERCISES

A.
1. Fifth Avenue . . . City.
2. The . . . Trumble Street on Tuesday.
3. Kim Wu . . . Pine Street in Reno.
4. The . . . Girand Avenue.
5. When . . . Constitution Avenue.
6. Shore Drive . . . construction.

B. Many . . . places. Roger Williams Avenue . . . Island. Brown Street . . . state. Other . . . people. That . . . Washington Street.

III. MAINTENANCE EXERCISES

A. Dag . . . Columbus Day. On Monday . . . school. Jason and Tomas . . . Phillips School. They . . . Ms. Johnson's room. On . . . Maynard School. Dag . . . basketball. He . . . Hartford.

B.
Langley Nurses Union
American Youth Soccer League
Explorers Club

Emerson Memorial Hospital
San Francisco Public Library
Hull House

C.
1. *Little Pear* . . .
2. *The Forest Pool* . . .
3. "Trees" . . . J. Kilmer.
4. I . . . I . . .

Prof.
Capt.
Supt.

Sat.
Aug.
Mon.

D.
Red Cross Aid
On Wednesday, February . . . Junior Red Cross. Our . . . Tileston School to Malaysia. Principal Reynolds . . . school. *The Tattler* . . . friends. We . . . Chairman White . . . Gateway Hotel . . . overseas. We . . . Valentine's Day . . . packed. We . . . February. Please . . . out.

Lesson 16: CAPITALIZING AND PUNCTUATING NAMES OF CITIES AND STATES

II. PRACTICE EXERCISES

1. Have . . . Hollywood, California?
2. We . . . Atlantic City, New Jersey, to Portland, Maine, . . . hours.
3. There . . . Paul Revere in Boston, Massachusetts.
4. Almost . . . Savannah, Georgia.
5. Many . . . New York City.
6. Plimoth Plantation . . . Plymouth, Massachusetts.
7. The . . . Chicago.
8. Do . . . Delores Gomez from San Antonio, Texas?
9. Does . . . Pittsburgh, Pennsylvania?
10. Did I . . . Hartford, Connecticut?
11. There . . . Paris, . . . Paris, Maine . . . Paris, Illinois.
12. Leo's . . . Cleveland Road, Denver, Colorado.

III. MAINTENANCE EXERCISES

A.
1. Our . . . Dodge Street, Cabot Street, and County Way.
2. Short Street . . . town.
3. My . . . Islington Road, Auburndale, Arizona.
4. Who . . . Pennsylvania Avenue?
5. The . . . Sacramento, California.
6. Bounty Way . . . Winding River Road.

B.
1. Have . . . Trixie . . . ?
2. The . . . Thomas A. Edison.
3. Get . . . now!
4. Look . . . down!
5. What . . . flag?
6. Our . . . Gerald Ford.

Lesson 17: WRITING STATE NAMES

II. PRACTICE EXERCISES

A.
1. D.C.
2. Ga.
3. S. Dak.
4. N.Y.
5. Nev.
6. N.J.
7. W. Va.
8. N.C.
9. S.C.
10. Md.

B.
1. Ala. . . . **AL**
2. Alaska . . . **AK**
3. Ariz. . . . **AZ**
4. Ark. . . . **AR**
5. Del. . . . **DE**
6. Hawaii . . . **HI**
7. Idaho . . . **ID**
8. Ill. . . . **IL**
9. Ind. . . . **IN**
10. Mass. . . . **MA**
11. Mich. . . . **MI**
12. Miss. . . . **MS**
13. Mo. . . . **MO**
14. Minn. . . . **MN**
15. Mont. . . . **MT**
16. Nebr. . . . **NE**
17. Ohio . . . **OH**
18. Okla. . . . **OK**
19. Oreg. . . . **OR**
20. Pa. . . . **PA**
21. Tenn. . . . **TN**
22. Tex. . . . **TX**
23. Utah . . . **UT**
24. Wash. . . . **WA**
25. Wis. . . . **WI**
26. Wyo. . . . **WY**

C.
1. Sharron's Diner
   122 Merchants Row
   Rutland, **VT** 05702

2. Ms. Laurie Watson
   251 Main Street
   Ellsworth, **ME** 04605

3. Mr. Juan Valdez
   755 Homer Avenue
   Kansas City, **KS** 66101

4. Mrs. Lillian Ryan
   25 Cottage Street
   Pawtucket, **RI** 02860

D.

849 Old Farm Road
Charlottesville, VA 22903
August 6, 1996

Dear Louise,

I . . . week. The . . . **Colorado** . . . **Wyoming** . . . interesting.
Our . . . **Connecticut** . . . reunion.
Thank you again.

Love,

Joanne

III. MAINTENANCE EXERCISES

1. Paula Pashko . . . Susan Douglas . . . California to **D.C.** in July.
2. My . . . Signal Street, Rochester, New Hampshire 03867.
3. Are . . . Silver Stationery Company in North Dakota?
4. The Lancaster Booster Club . . . Florida . . . Thanksgiving vacation.
5. Yes, I . . . Iowa . . . Tuesday, June 24.
6. I . . . *The Phantom Tollbooth* . . . Mexico.
7. Dr. Peabody's . . . Fraser Medical Building on Abbott Street.
8. Tell Father . . . I . . . me.
9. Will Capt. Manuela E. Ramos . . . Veterans Day parade?
10. When . . . Grandmother . . . New Orleans, Louisiana?

Lesson 18: CAPITALIZING NAMES OF COUNTRIES AND NATIONALITIES

II. PRACTICE EXERCISES

A.
1. <u>T</u>his . . . <u>E</u>nglish, <u>F</u>rench, and <u>S</u>panish.
2. <u>R</u>ed . . . <u>M</u>exican . . .
3. <u>T</u>he <u>C</u>hinese . . .
4. <u>V</u>incent . . . <u>S</u>tanley <u>E</u>xplorers <u>C</u>lub.
5. <u>T</u>he <u>P</u>uritans . . . <u>A</u>merica . . .
6. <u>T</u>he . . . <u>P</u>ersian . . . <u>I</u>ran.
7. <u>S</u>choolchildren . . . <u>J</u>unior <u>R</u>ed <u>C</u>ross.
8. <u>T</u>he <u>D</u>emocrats . . .
9. <u>M</u>any <u>J</u>apanese . . .

B.
2. **Pilgrims**
3. **Halloween**
4. no capital
5. **Sioux**
6. no capital
7. no capital
8. **Hispanics**
9. **Russians**
10. **Alaskans**
11. no capital
12. **Japanese**
13. **Indians**
14. no capital
15. no capital
16. **Americans**
17. no capital
18. **Brazilians**
19. **Cape Verdeans**
20. **Europeans**
21. **Mother's Day**
22. **Yemen**
23. no capital
24. **Germans**
25. **French**
26. **Asia**
27. **Puerto Ricans**
28. **American** history
29. **French** literature
30. no capital

III. MAINTENANCE EXERCISES

1. **Mr. Andrew P. Polanski**
   36 **Elm Street**
   Felton, DE 19943

2. **Professor Jesse A. Powers**
   71 **Lincoln Avenue**
   Trenton, NJ 08601

3. **Ms. Judy Gex**
   172 **Fergus Road**
   South Bend, IN 46624

4. **Chief Miguel Fernandez**
   2745 **Main Street**
   Hayward, CA 94540

5. **Dr. Karen L. Root**
   1545 **Roosevelt Avenue**
   Tampa, FL 33601

6. **Mrs. Buckley**
   River Drive
   Groton, CT 06340

_____ Lesson 19: LAST NAMES FIRST IN LISTS _____

II. PRACTICE EXERCISES

One point each for alphabetizing correctly.

3. **C**oatsworth, Elizabeth **J.**
4. **F**arjeon, **E**leanor
5. **L**ang, **A**ndrew
6. **McC**loskey, **R**obert
7. **M**ilne, **A. A.**

8. **P**yle, **H**oward
9. **S**awyer, **R**uth
10. **S**tevenson, **R**obert **L**ouis
11. **W**odehouse, **P. G.**

III. MAINTENANCE EXERCISES

A. 1. The **I**rish . . . orange.
    2. The **S**an **D**iego **M**arine **R**eserve . . . organization.
    3. The **A**merican **R**ed **C**ross . . . agency.
    4. The **S**alvation **A**rmy . . . needy.
    5. The **F**rench . . . **C**anada.
    6. **I**s **T**urkey . . . **E**ast?
    7. **C**hina and **J**apan . . . **O**rient.
    8. **M**y . . . **K**enya . . . **A**frican culture.
    9. **V**alentine's **D**ay . . . **F**ebruary 14.
   10. The **S**mithsonian **M**useum . . . **W**ashington, **D.C.**

B. Credit given for names only—not for addresses.

    1. **Mr. Raymond E. Martin**
    2. **Maura A. Powers, M.D.**
    3. **Mrs. Leona S. Lynch**

Lesson 20: COMMAS WITH WORDS IN SERIES
_____ AND GROUPS OF WORDS IN SERIES _____

II. PRACTICE EXERCISES

1. **K**ate, **T**ina, and **L**isa . . . team.
2. **M**ark . . . quickly, neatly, thoroughly, and correctly.
3. **T**he . . . short, interesting, and inspiring talk.

4. The . . . street, . . . gate, . . . yard, . . . house.
5. Wool, cotton, . . . here.
6. The . . . large, ripe, sweet, . . . juicy.
7. The . . . knit, spin, weave, and sew.
8. The . . . path, . . . field, . . . bridge.
9. The . . . large, new, . . . car.
10. There . . . you, Harry, . . . me.

III. MAINTENANCE EXERCISES

A. One point each for alphabetizing correctly.

1. Alcott, Louisa May
2. Ataturk, Kemal
3. Emerson, Ralph Waldo
4. Feynman, Richard
5. Frankfurter, Felix
6. Hurston, Zora Neale
7. Kahlo, Frida
8. Morrison, Toni
9. Paine, Thomas
10. Shakespeare, William

B.

165 Mason Street
Westfield, IL 62474
May 19, 1996

Dear Rama,

I . . . yesterday. I . . . corner.

Everyone . . . home. Do . . . school? What . . . like? When . . . Westfield? I . . . Mason Street. Be . . . me.

Your friend,
Allen

_____ Lesson 21: COMMAS WITH "YES" AND "NO" _____

II. PRACTICE EXERCISES

1. Yes, . . .   3. No, . . .   5. Well, . . .   7. Yes, . . .   9. Well, . . .
2. Oh, . . .   4. No, . . .   6. Yes, . . .   8. Oh, . . .   10. No, . . .

III. MAINTENANCE EXERCISES

A. 1. Yes, . . . you.
   2. Please . . . skis, boots, wax, . . . clothes.
   3. Oh, . . . try.
   4. I . . . camera, film, screen, projector, and case.
   5. They . . . math, science, . . . day.
   6. In . . . desks, maps, and chairs.
   7. Look, Theresa . . . sandwiches, milk, an apple, . . . lunch.
   8. Will . . . name, address, telephone number, father's name, and mother's name?

B. 1. Anderson, Jasmin
   2. Burdick, A. Myron
   3. Hanna, E. A.
   4. Smithson, Matthew Edwards
   5. Velez, Leonita R.

One point each for alphabetizing correctly.

C. 1. **M**y . . . **B**erlin, **N**ew **H**ampshire . . . **I** . . . **B**erlin, **C**onnecticut.
   2. The . . . **I** . . . **R**ita **C. B**lasi . . . elected.
   3. **W**ow! **W**hat a mistake!

_____ **Lesson 22: COMMAS WITH CONJUNCTIONS** _____

II. PRACTICE EXERCISES

A. 1. . . . , but **we** . . .   B. 2. . . . , **but** that . . .
   2. . . . , but **we** . . .   3. . . . handicap, **yet** it . . .
   3. . . . , and **you** . . .   4. . . . up, **or** you . . .
   4. . . . , or **you** . . .   5. . . . , **and I** . . .
   5. . . . , yet **we** . . .
   6. . . . , and **my** . . .
   7. . . . , or **we** . . .

III. MAINTENANCE EXERCISES

A. 1. Yes, . . . penguin.   6. No, . . . found.
   2. No, . . . it.   7. Oh, . . . crackers, cheese, nuts, . . . fruit.
   3. Oh, . . . know.   8. Well, . . . cold.
   4. Well, . . . be.   9. Yes, . . . true. ·
   5. Yes, . . . floor.   10. No, . . . understand.

B. 1. . . . **D**ecember, **J**anuary, . . . **F**ebruary.
   2. **S**kating, skiing, . . . **A**laska.
   3. **M**ae . . . exhibit.
   4. . . . **F**riend **B**ox **C**ompany, **W**atertown **C**hamber of **C**ommerce, . . .
      Ideal **S**hoe **S**tore . . . drive.
   5. **S**t. **P**atrick's **D**ay . . . **M**arch 17, . . .
      Valentine's **D**ay . . . **F**ebruary 14.
   6. . . . picnic.
   7. . . . **I** . . . tomorrow.

_____ **Lesson 23: COMMAS IN APPOSITIVES** _____

II. PRACTICE EXERCISES

1. Dr. Dolittle, an amazing man, . . .   6. Liz, her sister, . . .
2. . . . town, Puddleby-on-the-Marsh, . . .   7. . . . Ives, the teacher, . . .
3. . . . Jim, the shaggy dog, and Too-Too, . . . 8. Mr. Eagle, the automobile dealer, . . .
4. . . . wife, Queen Lioness, . . .   9. . . . Beauty, . . .
5. Robin, the main character, . . .   10. . . . movie, _The Wizard of Oz,_ . . .

III. MAINTENANCE EXERCISES

A. 1. . . . unwrapped, . . . see.
   2. . . . aching, . . . dentist.
   3. . . . eyesight, . . . hearing.
   4. . . . lunch, . . . cafeteria.
   5. . . . today, . . . late.

B. 1. . . . time, **but** Ned . . .
    2. . . . arrived, **and we** . . .
    3. . . . him, **but he** . . .
    4. . . . Louise, **and** then . . .
    5. . . . late, **but** Sean . . .

C. 1. **S**top, look, . . . street.
    2. **M**other and **F**ather . . . trip.
    3. **N**o, . . . town.
    4. **U**se . . . eyes, ears, . . . feet.
    5. **Y**es, . . . history.

Lesson 24: THE COMMA IN ADDRESS

II. PRACTICE EXERCISES

A. 1. Barbara, . . .
    2. . . . careful, Roy, . . .
    3. . . . time, . . .
    4. . . . here, dear, . . .
    5. . . . there, Ellen, . . .
    6. . . . jacket, . . .
    7. . . . ski, . . .
    8. No, Julie, . . .
    9. Jenny, . . .
    10. . . . skis, Ginny, . . .

B. 1. . . . flashlight, Esmeralda.
    2. . . . boys, Peter, . . . something.
    3. Yes, girls, . . . map?
    4. . . . here, Dusty.
    5. Here, Kitty, . . . milk.

III. MAINTENANCE EXERCISES

A. 1. . . . dog, a collie, . . .
    2. Spot, the spaniel, . . .
    3. Lorraine, my younger sister, . . .
    4. Mushak, the little puppy, . . .
    5. Sandy, the puppy's mother, . . .
    6. The storm, the . . . season, . . .
    7. Ms. González, the assistant, . . .
    8. Dr. Bennett, our principal, . . .
    9. Suzanne Hill, the captain, . . .
    10. . . . Terzian's, the paperback store, . . .

B. 1. **N**ew **E**ngland **P**ower **C**ompany
    2. **E**li **E. P**ettigrew, our director
    3. **C**apital **F**ood **S**tore
    4. **E**mpire **S**tate **B**uilding
    5. **P**rincipal **R**alph **H. D**oran
    6. no capitals

Lesson 25: DIRECT QUOTATIONS AT THE ENDS OF SENTENCES

II. PRACTICE EXERCISES

A. 1. **T**he . . . asked, "**W**hose . . . this?"
    2. **T**he . . . cried, "**T**he . . . falling!"
    3. **T**he . . . mourned, "**M**y . . . gold."
    4. **T**he . . . asked, "**W**hy . . . **I** . . . homely?"
    5. **T**he . . . shouted, "**O**h, my . . . sparks!"

B. 2. **M**rs. **S**imms asked, "**W**hat . . . next?"
    3. **A**lice . . . answered, "**I** . . . reading."
    4. **J**erry asked, "**W**hat . . . try?"
    5. **E**mma . . . enthusiasm, "**T**he . . . business!"
    6. **J**erry exclaimed, "**W**hat . . . are!"

III. MAINTENANCE EXERCISES

A. 1. When . . . meeting, **M**rs. **P**resident?
   2. The . . . **W**illiam, **J**oel, and **D**uncan.
   3. Thank you, class, . . . honor.
   4. The **M**c**C**abe **S**hoe **C**ompany . . . **D**allas, **T**exas.
   5. Come anytime, **D**r. **S**mith, . . .
   6. **O**kera, . . . you.

B.   **M**other, **F**rank, **F**ather, . . . **I** . . . automobiles. This . . . **C**oncord, **P**rovidence, **H**artford, . . . **N**ew **Y**ork **C**ity. As . . . **I** . . . choke, sputter, . . . wheeze. **M**ayor **W**ells . . . **P**resident **M**ercedez **S**antana . . . **A**ntique **A**utomobile **A**ssociation. The . . . cranks, . . . cars, . . . crowds, . . . road.

Lesson 26: DIRECT QUOTATIONS AT THE BEGINNINGS OF SENTENCES

II. PRACTICE EXERCISES

A. 1. "We . . . time," . . . **J**im quickly.
   2. "**J**im, . . . junk?" . . . **J**ack.
   3. "We . . . garage," **J**im . . . him.
   4. "**J**im, . . . pile!" . . . **J**ack.
   5. "When . . . collecting?" . . . **J**im.
   6. "**J**im, . . . now," . . . **J**ack.
   7. "**M**agazines . . . money," . . . **J**im.
   8. "**J**im, . . . first?" . . . **J**ack.
   9. "**E**xactly!" . . . **J**im.
   10. "We're off!" . . . **J**ack.

B. 2. "How . . . here," . . . explorers.
   3. "Will . . . moon?" . . . astronaut.
   4. "Here . . . suit," . . . captain.
   5. "**Q**uite . . . it?" . . . navigator.

III. MAINTENANCE EXERCISES

A. See your teacher for corrections. One point for each correctly written quotation.

B. 1. **J**anet said, "**M**y . . . home."
   2. "Is . . . dog-sitter?" **A**nika asked.
   3. **J**anet answered, "**I** . . . know, . . . **I**'ve . . . caterers."
   4. "**I**'ve . . . everything!" **C**huck exclaimed.
   5. **J**anet replied, "**O**h, what . . . next?"

C. 1. Hey look! **D**id . . . **C**aptain **W**ylie caught?
   2. The **F**rench . . . **A**merican soldier.
   3. Many . . . **P**ilgrims . . . **E**ngland.
   4. Put . . . barrel, **G**ail.
   5. *Tom Sawyer* . . . book, . . . *Huckleberry Finn* better.
   6. Some . . . books, . . . them.
   7. **M**other and **F**ather . . . party.
   8. Wow! This . . . yet.

II. PRACTICE EXERCISES

A. 1. "**K**en," reminded **F**ather, "this . . . once."
    2. "**P**lease," **K**en begged, "may **I** . . . longer?"
    3. "**T**his yard," replied **M**r. **C**hin, "is . . . disgrace."
    4. "**W**ell," asked **K**en, "is . . . job?"
    5. "**S**on," demanded **M**r. **C**hin, "you . . . business."

B. 1. "**O**nce," said **R**uth, "we . . . away."
    2. "**T**hen," asked **T**eresa, "did . . . house?"
    3. "**S**he came," **R**uth laughed, "and . . . call."
    4. "**W**hen . . . rang," asked **T**eresa, "what . . . do?"
    5. "**S**he . . . receiver," **R**uth said, "and . . . disappointed."

III. MAINTENANCE EXERCISES

A. 1. "**M**ay **I** . . . tires?" . . . **K**arin.
    2. "**H**elp yourself," . . . said, "but . . . through."
    3. **K**arin asked, "Is . . . station?"
    4. "**O**nly . . . time," . . . attendant.
    5. "**W**ell, . . . favor," . . . **K**arin.

B. Brink, Carol **R.**   *Baby Island*
    Emily, Douglas **R.**   *Appleseed Farm*
    Field, Rachel **L.**   *Taxis and Toadstools*
    Perkins, Lucy **F.**   *The Dutch Twins*

C. 1. The Wilderness Club . . . Mirror Lake Hotel this afternoon.
    2. The Greensboro Community Chorus . . . Sunday, March 14 . . .
    3. The Shelton Chamber of Commerce . . . town.

Spring Fever

I . . .
It . . .
Whenever I can, I . . .
My . . .

_____ Lesson 28:   THE INDIRECT QUOTATION _____

II. PRACTICE EXERCISES

A. 1. **D**eena . . . home.
    2. "**G**o home, **A**ndy," said **D**eena.
    3. **S**he . . . **C**ecila . . . her.
    4. "**I** . . . him," . . . **C**ecila.
    5. **I** . . . way.
    6. **D**eena . . . days.
    7. **C**ecila . . . share.
    8. **T**he . . . all.

B. 1. a. Debbie said, "Jump . . . bush."
   b. Debbie said to jump over the bush.

2. a. Nina replied, "I don't want to because I am wearing new pants."
   b. Nina . . . pants.

3. a. "Then . . . me," . . . Debbie, "as I do it."
   b. Debbie suggested that Nina watch as she did it.

4. a. "That was a pretty good trick," agreed Nina.
   b. Nina . . . trick.

III. MAINTENANCE EXERCISES

A. 1. "Come . . . over, Julio, . . . bike," . . . Carlos.
   2. Julio . . . day.
   3. Then Julio . . . Carlos . . . working.
   4. "When . . . me," . . . Carlos, "I . . . loose."
   5. My uncle, Eduardo Salas, at the Maple Street Garage . . . you.
   6. Is . . . garage, Julio, . . . Elm Street and Park Place?

B. 1. Sylvester Speer, . . . husband, . . . Monday, Tuesday, Wednesday, and Thursday.
   2. Did Father . . . *Mutiny on the Bounty* by Nordhoff . . . Hall?
   3. Selectman George E. Moore . . . F. H. Lily Company.
   4. "The Orlando Boosters Club . . . Colts . . . year," . . . Miles.
   5. "Will . . . now, Sally, . . . meeting?" . . . Mother.

——————————————— Lesson 29: WRITING CONVERSATION ———————————————

II. PRACTICE EXERCISES

A.   ➡ means new paragraph. One point for each paragraph.

   ➡ "I . . . yesterday," Henry said.
   ➡ Jean asked, "Did . . . anything?"
   ➡ "I . . . I . . . boat. It . . . overboard," . . . Henry.
   ➡ Jean asked if he got wet.
   ➡ "No," laughed Henry, "I . . . back."

B.   ➡ means new paragraph.

   ➡ "How . . . river?" asked Al.
   ➡ Tania answered, "My . . . down."
   ➡ "But . . . enough," . . . Al.
   ➡ "I'll build one," shouted Tania, "or . . . I'll . . . shoes."

III. MAINTENANCE EXERCISES

A. 1. "The . . . bad," . . . Andre, "that . . . drive."
   2. "Oh," . . . Walter, "is . . . outside?"
   3. "Yes," he replied, "cars . . . road."
   4. "In that case," . . . Walter, "it . . . home."
   5. "The . . . tomorrow," said Andre, "so . . . all."

B. 1. We'll . . . Martha and Marita, the twins . . . street.
2. Mother said, "Yes, . . . Father . . . car."
3. The American Heart Association . . . February.
4. "We . . . Lang's Supply," . . . leader.
5. Hooray! We'll . . . now.

_____ Lesson 30: **THE APOSTROPHE IN CONTRACTIONS** _____

II. PRACTICE EXERCISES

A. 1. can't   4. won't   7. hadn't   10. Who's   13. hasn't
    2. Don't   5. wasn't   8. aren't   11. she'd   14. That's
    3. aren't   6. I'll   9. didn't   12. We'll   15. Let's

B. 1. does not   4. he will   8. they have   12. were not
    2. they are   5. you will   9. we are   13. I am
    3. you have   6. could not   10. he is   14. she is
                     7. it is   11. had not

III. MAINTENANCE EXERCISES

A.   ➡ means new paragraph. One point for each paragraph.

    ➡ "That . . . officer," said Fred, "took . . . ball, bat, . . . glove."
    ➡ "How . . . happen?" . . . Dr. Carter.
    ➡ "My . . . I . . . street," . . . Fred.
    ➡ "Didn't . . . reason?" . . . Dr. Carter.
    ➡ "Well, yes," answered Fred. "He . . . law. This . . . ball, bat, . . . glove."

B. **Dr. Laski**   **Representative Maceda**   a stamp club
    A. J. Wolsky   **Pres. Wanda Butman**   **Boy Scouts of America**

C. 1. . . . United States, China, Japan, . . . meeting.
    2. Volcanoes, lakes, waterfalls, . . . beautiful.
    3. "Hurry . . . bed," . . . Mother.
    4. . . . replied, "We . . . bed."

_____ Lesson 31: **THE APOSTROPHE IN SINGULAR POSSESSIVES** _____

II. PRACTICE EXERCISES

A. 1. Arthur's
    2. man's
    3. boy's
    4. beaver's
    5. sister's
    6. computer's
    7. Roma's
    8. shuttle's
    9. choir's
    10. woman's

B. 2. Consuelo's
    3. squirrel's
    4. Ross's
    5. Claire's
    6. Mrs. Tsung's
    7. captain's
    8. fire fighter's
    9. Helena's
    10. girl's

III. MAINTENANCE EXERCISES

A.
1. It's . . . up, Alex, isn't it?
2. . . . doesn't he?
3. Mother said, "I wouldn't . . .
4. Nathan, . . . haven't . . .
5. Juana, we're . . .
6. Doesn't . . .
7. They're . . . aren't they?
8. Wasn't . . .
9. We won't . . . you, . . .
10. Couldn't . . .

B. Check with your teacher for corrections.
One point for each correctly written answer.

C.
1. Yes, . . . bananas.
2. When, for heaven's sake, . . . that?
3. . . . begged, "Please . . . Saturday?"
4. "I . . . time," . . . Mother.
5. "If . . . school," . . . Axel, "then . . . go?"

_____ Lesson 32:   THE APOSTROPHE IN PLURAL POSSESSIVES _____

II. PRACTICE EXERCISES

A.
1. boys'
2. girls'
3. scouts'
4. Joneses'
5. ponies'
6. horses'
7. women's
8. stars'
9. Children's

B.
1. children's
2. mice's
3. deer's
4. geese's
5. beginners'
6. women's
7. fire fighters'
8. police officers'

III. MAINTENANCE EXERCISES

A.
1. Alfred's
2. boys
3. boys'
4. puppy's
5. aunt's
6. dog's
7. announcer's
8. truck's
9. neighbor's
10. fire fighters'

B.
it will
I am
would not
should not
will not
we will
you will
we have

C.
1. "Parts of an Airplane"
   "Watching the Weather"
   "In the Control Tower"
   "A Trip in a Jet"
2. . . . Pine Tree Road . . . Mother and Father.
3. The English, French, and Dutch . . . America.
4. The . . .
   Amato, Victor P.
   Montez, Blanca R.
   Ector, A. H.
   Hayes, E. Cicely
5. A dog's . . . days.
6. Doug's . . . office.
7. The children's . . . crowded.

D. "I don't . . . time," . . . cousin. "Why don't . . . me?"
"I . . . to," . . . mouse.
At . . . cousin's . . . food. "This is wonderful," . . . mouse. "I . . . forever."
Just . . . appeared. Frightened . . . shelter.

Lesson 33: CAPITALIZING GEOGRAPHICAL TERMS (RIVERS, OCEANS, MOUNTAINS, AND CONTINENTS)

II. PRACTICE EXERCISES

A.
1. White Mountains
2. Ashley River
3. Aegean Sea
4. Charles River
5. none
6. none
7. none
8. Europe
9. none
10. South America
11. none
12. Asia
13. Adirondack Mountains
14. none
15. Atlantic Ocean
16. Ohio River
17. Pikes Peak
18. Africa

B. We're . . . Asia . . . It's . . . Egyptians . . . Nile River. The Chinese . . . Today . . . Europe. This . . . Atlantic Ocean . . . United States. It's . . . Mississippi River . . . Rocky Mountains.

III. MAINTENANCE EXERCISES

A.
2. citizens'
3. redcoats'
4. messenger's
5. general's
6. soldiers'

B.
1. Memorial Day
2. . . . April
3. Vietnamese
4. Sri Lanka
5. Thursday . . .
6. Ms. Lucia M. Rivera

C.
1. . . . soups, salads, casseroles, . . .
2. . . . boy's . . .
3. It's . . . up, Angela, isn't it?

Lesson 34: CAPITALIZING GEOGRAPHICAL TERMS (REGIONS AND SECTIONS)

II. PRACTICE EXERCISES

A.
1. none
2. Connecticut
3. West
4. none
5. none
6. none
7. none
8. none
9. North Dakota
10. none
11. none
12. North
13. South
14. West Indies
15. none

B.
1. Much . . . South.
2. In . . .
3. Sugar . . . West . . . Southwest.
4. Winters . . .
5. The . . .

III. MAINTENANCE EXERCISES

A.
1. The Colorado River . . . Arizona . . . New Mexico.
2. The . . . United States . . . Mount McKinley.
3. Have . . . Redson River . . .
4. Much . . . Puget Sound . . . Washington.
5. The Suez Canal . . . Red Sea . . . Mediterranean.

B. See your teacher for corrections. One point for each correctly written name.

C. 1. . . . "I . . . it."
   2. "I . . . you," . . .
   3. none
   4. "Where . . . going," . . . Andrea, "that . . . you?"

———————————————— **Lesson 35: THE COLON** ————————————————

II. PRACTICE EXERCISES

A. 10:30   9:05   6:00   3:05   11:45

B. 2. 8:30 **P.M.**
   3. 2:00 **A.M.**
   4. 6:15 **P.M.**
   5. 7:45 **A.M.**

C. 1. . . . New York . . . times: 8:20 **A.M.**, 12:00 noon, . . . 3:20 **P.M.**
   2. . . . books: *Famous Women, Historical Heroes,* and *Book of Myths.*
   3. . . . store: bread, milk, cheese, . . . eggs.
   4. . . . 1:45 **P.M.**, . . . 2:30 **P.M.**
   5. . . . 3:05 **P.M.**

III. MAINTENANCE EXERCISES

1. The . . . April 2, 1902, in Los Angeles.
2. "Dad, will . . . golf?" . . . Olivia.
3. Mrs. Carr, the . . . teacher, . . . watercolors.
4. "Oh, Eric," Marilyn . . . kitchen, "help me! My . . . over!"
5. Denise, the Canadian . . . class, . . . French.
6. On June 1, 1954, if Congress . . . Armistice Day to Veterans Day.
7. Do . . . East . . . West?
8. Dr. A. J. Djar . . . Minnesota Department of Wildlife . . . Monday at 9:30 **A.M.** . . . conservation.
9. "Hilda . . . *The Giving Tree,* and I . . . *Treasure Island,*" . . . Matt.
10. Dr. Audrey Chapman-Steele . . . Africa . . . American Museum of Natural History.

DICTATION

LESSON 1

a. 1. We will go with you.
2. Please hold the door.
3. She held the dog firmly.
4. I can not eat any more.
5. Pass your papers to the front of the room.

b. 1. Ask your friend to come with us.
2. I will hold the door.
3. Keep to the right.
4. He ate the last slice.
5. They have finished their work.

LESSON 2

a. 1. Where did you find my pen?
2. Stop that thief!
3. Is this hers or his?
4. Did you invite anyone else?
5. We are sinking!

b. 1. Who returned this book?
2. Help! The shelf is falling!
3. Why did she arrive so late?
4. Where is my other boot?
5. Hurry and call the doctor!

LESSON 3

a. 1. Oh, he will do it.
2. My goodness, this is too slow.
3. Ow! That hurts.
4. Ah, that tastes better.
5. Well, I can try.

b. 1. Well, the time has come.
2. Ah, that looks just right.
3. Good grief, you broke them!
4. Oh, they will return it tomorrow.
5. Ouch! It bit me.

LESSON 4

a. Write the abbreviations for:
1. Mrs.
2. (Thursday)—Thurs.
3. (Avenue)—Ave.
4. (October)—Oct.
5. (pound)—lb

b. Write the abbreviations for:
1. (Mister)—Mr.
2. (Friday)—Fri.
3. (Street)—St.
4. (November)—Nov.
5. (ounce)—oz

LESSON 5

a. 1. P. T. Barnum was a circus man.
2. His name was G. Roberto Perez.
3. Father works for Charlene Peters.
4. The name on the office door was John D. Powers.
5. Everyone should know who F.D.R. was.

b. 1. Ms. Zina is the leader.
2. Her name is R. Mary Jones.
3. The name he gave was Albert T. Black.
4. Her name was given as Anna V. Horwitz.
5. One president was referred to as L.B.J.

DICTATION

LESSON 6

a. 1. The parade was led by General Raymond Clarke. (Gen.)
2. Did she call Doctor Vanessa Nelson? (Dr.)
3. The bill was signed by Treasurer James Pilsa. (Treas.)
4. He listened to Senator Vincent Martino. (Sen.)
5. The speech was given by Governor Dolores Cordero. (Gov.)

b. 1. The column was led by Captain Morgan Stavos. (Capt.)
2. The interview was given by Professor Rodrigo Higuera. (Prof.)
3. The talk was made by President Charles Johns. (Pres.)
4. The meeting was opened by Representative Irene LaCosta. (Rep.)
5. Will you speak to Doctor John Smith? (Dr.)

LESSON 7

a. 1. Have you read *Black Beauty*?
2. I find interesting pictures in the magazine *National Photography*.
3. Do you read the comics in the *Medfield Times*?
4. I have read *David Copperfield* many times.
5. I enjoyed the poem "Slippery Slope" in our textbook.

b. 1. The *Incredible Journey* was very exciting.
2. I find many current events in each issue of *This Week*.
3. Did you do the crossword puzzle in the *Independent News*?
4. When I was younger, I enjoyed the "Jack and Jill" stories.
5. *Silver Song* is a collection of poems for children.

LESSON 8

a. 1. When the clouds of the morn
   To the west fly away,
   You may depend
   On a fair settled day.

2. In winter I get up at night,
   And dress by yellow candlelight.
   In summer quite the other way,
   I have to go to bed by day.

b. 1. Spades take up leaves
   No better than spoons,
   And bags full of leaves
   Are light as balloons.

2. Roads go on forever
   Over rock and under tree,
   By caves where sun has never shone,
   By streams that never find the sea.

LESSON 9

a. 1. I gave my book to Mother.
2. My father would not take me to the game.
3. Did you see my mother?
4. I will ask Father if I can go.
5. Mother and Father did not like that movie.

b. 1. Please tell my mother all about the accident.
2. I want my father to tell Mother about it.
3. Did you bake that bread for your mother?
4. Why doesn't Father hurry home?
5. Have your mother and father been on a vacation?

LESSON 10

a. 1. Do you think I can do it?
2. That book is not the one I have read.
3. I would like to go to the party.
4. Did I answer the question correctly?
5. You and I do not think alike.

b. 1. I have not been able to finish my work.
2. You and I might work together.
3. Do you believe I told the truth?
4. I think I may stay at home today.
5. The doctor told me I had the measles.

DICTATION

LESSON 11

a. 1. She bought tools at Apex.
   2. Do you ever shop at Horners?
   3. Why is the Book Corner closed today?
   4. Does his mother work for Novotech?
   5. I buy my food at the Sun Market

b. 1. The Pax Bakery is a small store.
   2. My favorite yogurt is Healthform.
   3. Her father works for Universal Airlines.
   4. Do you ever shop at the Spendthrift?
   5. The book was bought at Hathaway Book Shop.

LESSON 12

a. 1. They visited the United Nations last week.
   2. Have you seen Independence Hall?
   3. That man swam the English Channel.
   4. The class took a trip to the Boston Museum of Science.
   5. We will visit the new park.

b. 1. Are you a student at the Montessori School?
   2. I have climbed the Washington Monument.
   3. My favorite building is the Lincoln Memorial.
   4. Where is the Hanover Inn?
   5. They have never been to Marineland.

LESSON 13

a. 1. Do you belong to the Boy Scouts?
   2. The chorus sang last night.
   3. My mother enjoys the camera club.
   4. His brother has joined the U.S. Marines.
   5. The Celtics lost their game last night.

b. 1. The L.A. Dodgers are in town.
   2. The Ashville Computer Club held its meeting last week.
   3. Did you go camping with the Girl Scouts?
   4. My sister worked at Star Software when she finished college.
   5. The skating club will put on a show.

LESSON 14

a. 1. School begins near Labor Day.
   2. Did you go swimming last Wednesday?
   3. What will you do for Columbus Day weekend?
   4. How do you celebrate the Fourth of July?
   5. On Saturday he will go to the ball game.

b. 1. I have my music lesson on Monday.
   2. We had a party on Valentine's Day.
   3. Do you stay for sports on Friday afternoon?
   4. On November 11, we observe Veterans Day.
   5. There is a parade on Thanksgiving Day.

DICTATION

LESSON 15
a. 1. When did you move to Park Avenue?
   2. Main Street is a busy place.
   3. Shall we walk down Glen Avenue?
   4. How long did you live at Smith Lane?
   5. There is a lot of mud on Willow Road.

b. 1. The next street is Black Street.
   2. He moved into a house on Stevens Road.
   3. His father's office is on Summer Street.
   4. That short lane has many trees.
   5. Forest Street is behind our school.

LESSON 16
a. 1. Ms. Anna Penn moved to 22 Main Street, Dover, Maryland.
   2. How long have you lived in New York?
   3. We hope to go to California this summer.
   4. Portland is in Maine and Oregon.
   5. The Pilgrims landed at Plymouth.

b. 1. A great deal of cotton comes from Texas.
   2. Did you ever receive any fruit from Florida?
   3. Chicago is a large city.
   4. Hartford is the capital of Connecticut.
   5. Mr. Ross Tello will meet you at 159 Sixth Street, Irving, Texas.

LESSON 17
a. Write the standard state and postal abbreviations for:
   1. Vermont (Vt., VT)
   2. Maine (Maine, ME)
   3. Kansas (Kans., KS)
   4. Rhode Island (R.I., RI)
   5. Virginia (Va., VA)

b. Write the standard state and postal abbreviations for:
   1. Georgia (Ga., GA)
   2. Illinois (Ill., IL)
   3. Nevada (Nev., NV)
   4. North Carolina (N.C., NC)
   5. Mississippi (Miss., MS)

LESSON 18
a. 1. He is a citizen of France.
   2. Have you ever traveled through Canada?
   3. Alaska was the forty-ninth state.
   4. The Indians live beside the river.
   5. Dutch soil is fine for tulips.

b. 1. I enjoyed my trip to Hawaii.
   2. Some Chinese live on boats called junks.
   3. Did you ever see Spanish dancers in Spain?
   4. I had fun exploring the caves in Virginia.
   5. The Swiss make lovely clocks.

LESSON 19
a. 1. Camp, Peter E.
   2. Dennis, Mary S.
   3. Mills, F. F.
   4. Potter, A. Rebecca
   5. Smart, Maxwell

b. 1. Lopez, J. Marcos
   2. McCabe, Jamie
   3. Rivera, Y. D.
   4. Wood, Lauren
   5. Young, B. B.

DICTATION

LESSON 20

a. 1. Myra, Sue, and Jane are going to Baltimore.
   2. I climbed over the fence, under the bushes, and into the hole.
   3. Did you invite Bill, Rico, and Tom to the party?
   4. She saw a brief, amusing, and colorful movie.
   5. Oranges, lemons, and grapefruit are citrus fruits.

b. 1. What is round, blue, small, and shiny?
   2. The dentist will check Allison, Eric, and Fred.
   3. Turn the key, lift the latch, and open the door.
   4. A cute, fluffy, tiny kitten was on the porch.
   5. History, math, and spelling are my favorite studies.

LESSON 21

a. 1. Yes, I will go with you.
   2. No, I do not need any books.
   3. Oh, I forgot my keys.
   4. Yes, your package is ready.
   5. No, you cannot go out and play.

b. 1. Well, you had no reason to be in that room.
   2. Yes, you may wear your new coat.
   3. No, his team did not win last night.
   4. Yes, we went to New York for a vacation.
   5. No, we have no more milk.

LESSON 22

a. 1. We rode in the bus, and we saw the game.
   2. Sonya passed the juice, and I passed the snacks.
   3. You may come in, but the party has not started.
   4. He went to Houston, and he saw a show.
   5. She came to school, but she was not feeling well.

b. 1. We may go to town, or we may stay at home.
   2. You could play ball, or you might prefer to read.
   3. You hold it, and I will cut it.
   4. I would like to go with you, but I have no time.
   5. She will agree, yet she cannot help.

LESSON 23

a. 1. Marlene, my best friend, is visiting.
   2. He was playing football, his favorite game.
   3. Rex, my dog, likes to chase cars.
   4. Did you give that book to Ms. Barton, your teacher?
   5. Cranston, a city in Rhode Island, is south of Providence.

b. 1. Liam, the captain, called the plays for the game.
   2. I go to Florida in winter, our cold season.
   3. Willis, my brother, is going to camp.
   4. Did you see Rosanna, the famous skater?
   5. She picked a rose, her favorite flower.

DICTATION

LESSON 24   a. 1. Nellie, where is your hat?
    2. Take a turn, Ming, after your sister.
    3. I have no more, Benito.
    4. Betty, call me when you find it.
    5. Is this yours, Ed, or does it belong to Jeff?

    b. 1. May I have another one, Dad?
    2. Tim, I will wait for you.
    3. Hold tight, Maro, hold tight!
    4. Where is the car parked, Mom?
    5. Matt, hold the rope.

LESSON 25   a. 1. Mrs. Smith answered, "Mary will not be at school today."
    2. Heidi said, "Please throw the ball to me."
    3. Marla asked, "Will you go to the show?"
    4. Erin gasped, "My throat is very sore."
    5. Jake asked, "May I look at your book?"

    b. 1. The teacher scolded, "We have too many late pupils."
    2. The president replied, "I have no comment."
    3. The umpire shouted, "Strike out!"
    4. Phil said, "My cat had kittens last night."
    5. Laurie asked, "Is my bike ready to use?"

LESSON 26   a. 1. "That is a pretty picture," said Juan.
    2. "Do you like to ski?" asked June.
    3. "I am very hungry," replied Alexandra.
    4. "Dinner is ready," called Dad.
    5. "Which car do you like?" asked Father.

    b. 1. "There are six students absent," the teacher said.
    2. "Where were you yesterday?" asked Mr. Merlino.
    3. "I was ill yesterday," replied Bethan.
    4. "You must return my book," demanded Saul.
    5. "I have so much work to do," sighed Kim.

LESSON 27   a. 1. "I am tired," said Doug, "and I want to go to bed."
    2. "That robin," said Mother, "is the first one I've seen this spring."
    3. "That picture," remarked Dad, "is too big for the wall."
    4. "Can you open the door," asked Beverly, "without a key?"
    5. "This cheese is good," said Mara as she took another slice.

    b. 1. "Did you read," asked Father, "about that flying object?"
    2. "I will go," agreed Seth, "if you will drive me."
    3. "That book," said Ingrid, "is very hard for me to read."
    4. "I want to go," said Pablo, "but I need a ride."
    5. "Those dishes," hinted Father, "will not wash themselves."

DICTATION

LESSON 28

a. 1. Franco called his dog.
2. Dad asked if anyone wanted to help.
3. Janice said that Debbie was having a party.
4. "Were you invited?" asked Donna.
5. The newspaper explained the facts.

b. 1. The coach asked the boys to help.
2. "She will not be ready," replied Betty.
3. The baby said something we did not understand.
4. Her sister called me.
5. He replied that he would wait.

LESSON 29

a. "Are you going to the party tonight?" asked Toki.
"I will have to ask my mother first," said Dick, "but I believe she will let me."
"Would you like to come with us?" Toki asked Kurt.
"I am sorry, but I have to work," replied Kurt. "Maybe I can go another time."

b. "Mary is having a party," said Katrina.
"Yes," added Sue, "and I am planning to go, but I don't know what to take for a present."
"I am taking a book," said Katrina, "because I know she enjoys reading."
"That is a good idea," remarked Sue. "No one ever has too many books."

LESSON 30

a. 1. Wouldn't you like to go on a picnic today?
2. Merrill couldn't finish the jigsaw puzzle.
3. Won't you please help me with my homework tonight?
4. I can't help worrying about that lost dog.
5. That red shirt doesn't look right on that man.

b. 1. This isn't a very hot day.
2. My dog won't stay out of the street.
3. We aren't going to let you go far away.
4. Couldn't you make less noise?
5. That man wasn't the one I thought he was.

LESSON 31

a. 1. A boy's hat fell into the mud.
2. The dog's collar was lost.
3. I heard the school's bell ringing.
4. That girl's game was canceled.
5. Her picture was on the book's cover.

b. 1. My cat's dish is empty.
2. The sheep's coat was very heavy.
3. The car's tires spun in the snow.
4. Ellen went to her friend's house.
5. The boys ran toward the bank's sign.

DICTATION

LESSON 32

a. 1. The farmer held the mice's tails.
  2. All the pillows' feathers were soft.
  3. The oxen's yoke was very heavy.
  4. Five students' reports were missing.
  5. Spies' tactics must be clever.

b. 1. All of the axes' handles were broken.
  2. Two girls' artwork was on display.
  3. Why were the men's coats torn?
  4. They bought some children's toys.
  5. The rescuers were presented with heroes' medals.

LESSON 33

a. 1. Ten explorers were climbing the Alps.
  2. Walter took a trip to the Nile.
  3. We flew over the Pacific Ocean.
  4. There are six states in New England.
  5. Do you know anyone from Africa?

b. 1. Tom Sawyer lived on the Mississippi.
  2. I am glad I live in North America.
  3. It would be fun to ride a camel in Egypt.
  4. The water in the Arctic must be very cold.
  5. She once climbed Mount Washington.

LESSON 34

a. 1. Have you ever been in the West?
  2. I am interested in the Indians of the Northwest.
  3. Alaska is our newest northern state.
  4. Is the East colder in the winter?
  5. Her grandmother goes south for the winter.

b. 1. The North African spoke English very well.
  2. We will visit southern France very soon.
  3. Does the South have the same type of weather as the West?
  4. The west bank of the river is sandy.
  5. Does this road go north and south or east and west?

LESSON 35

(Write these times as numbers.)

a. 1. eleven thirty in the morning (11:30 A.M.)
  2. quarter past three in the afternoon (3:15 P.M.)
  3. twenty minutes of six in the evening (5:40 P.M.)
  4. one o'clock in the morning (1:00 A.M.)
  5. quarter of eight in the evening (7:45 P.M.)

b. 1. half past nine in the morning (9:30 A.M.)
  2. quarter of two in the afternoon (1:45 P.M.)
  3. ten ten in the evening (10:10 P.M.)
  4. twenty-five minutes of three in the morning (2:35 A.M.)
  5. quarter past seven in the evening (7:15 P.M.)

POST TEST ONE

Directions: Capitalize and punctuate where necessary.

A. 1. ms Diane DeVito would like to meet pres Simone Levesque

2. well I just don't believe that you would do that

3. help let's move these fence posts

4. why did the girls kick the soccer ball that far

5. does she live on the same street as mr Avakian

Directions: Abbreviate the underlined words.

B. 1. Monday, Tuesday, Friday, October

2. Doctor Rostow

3. 26 miles, 385 yards, no feet or inches

4. the eighth hour, the third year

5. Ms. Stokes, President of the Felt Company

POST TEST TWO

Directions: Capitalize and punctuate where necessary.

1. j r richards, the pitcher, has an excellent fastball

2. senator marc brady and senator elizabeth romero met briefly

3. the magazines sports today and national explorer have great photographs

4. the book that ms carol stokes wrote was called u s energy conservation

5. rose, where did you find the book where the sidewalk ends by shel silverstein

6. secretary of state edwin arlen worried about the Mideast

7. was representative kim davis reelected

8. the worldwide book of world records is always a best-seller

9. dr helen kinsella and mother discussed the problem

10. the new roller skates belong to l c greenwood

POST TEST THREE

Directions: Capitalize, punctuate, and underline where necessary.

1. the los angeles lakers have won the nba championship

2. the denver symphony orchestra is known worldwide

3. united motors has offices in all fifty states

4. what is robert e lee's middle name

5. the southeastern solar energy company has a new invention

6. the hardware sale at hammersmiths is over

7. she joined the staff of colt computers

8. quiet there is no talking allowed in the u s senate gallery

9. i read about ungo's food specialties in an issue of gourmet

10. the league of nations was dissolved in 1946

POST TEST FOUR

Directions: Correct the following sentences by putting capital letters over small letters where you think they are needed. Insert punctuation marks to make the sentences complete. Remember what you learned in lessons fourteen through eighteen. Check your work before handing it in.

1. was the assembly program on monday or tuesday

2. what were the plans for the thanksgiving program

3. the team from front street played football against the team from back street on columbus day

4. hartford connecticut, is just about halfway between boston massachusetts, and new york city

5. the pilgrims and the puritans came to america from england

6. parties were held in all classes on halloween

7. my address is 9 brewster avenue eureka kansas 67045

8. the capital of the united states is washington d c

POST TEST FIVE

Directions: On the lines provided write the following list of names in alphabetical order with the last name first.

A. 1. francis scott key   1. _____

    2. zebulon pike   2. _____

    3. henry ford   3. _____

    4. pablo picasso   4. _____

    5. ernest hemingway   5. _____

    6. camille saint-saëns   6. _____

Directions: In the following sentences the commas have been left out. Remembering what you have learned in lessons nineteen through twenty-three, insert the commas where needed to correct the sentences.

B. 1. Spring summer autumn and winter are the four seasons.

    2. We traveled in Nebraska Wyoming South Dakota North Dakota and Manitoba.

    3. Yes every nation needs a flag.

    4. No I think the white stars should be on a blue field.

    5. The cactus a desert plant needs a lot of sunlight and it should not be watered often.

    6. Mr. Brown the storekeeper is all out of milk today but he has juice in the refrigerator.

Name _____

POST TEST SIX

Directions: Capitalize, punctuate, and underline where necessary.

1. nina said do you know how to drive

2. the paints papers and negatives are in the art room

3. esther said mother clean the garage, please

4. nora and bob caught perch eel and trout while fishing

5. officer i believe that my little brother is lost

6. many of the students had read the hobbit by j r r tolkien

7. well how am i going to get out of here

8. ladies the tour guide said follow me

9. we plan to be in beaufort by morning

10. yoko asked is that the correct pronunciation

P
O
S
T

T
E
S
T

Name _____

POST TEST SEVEN

Directions: In the blank in each of the following sentences write the contraction for the words in parentheses.

A. 1. (Here is) _____ a new story for you, Petra.

2. (I would) _____ like to hear a story!

3. (Will not) _____ you tell it to me now?

4. (What is) _____ it about?

5. (It is) _____ a story without words.

Directions: Place an apostrophe where needed in each underlined word in the following sentences.

B. 1. Several <u>childrens</u> parents arrived late.

2. The <u>babys</u> rattle makes a loud noise.

3. My <u>ponys</u> face is white.

4. <u>Birds</u> songs are cheery.

5. <u>Lauras</u> stamp collection won first prize.

POST TEST EIGHT

Directions: Place the proper punctuation marks and capital letters where they are needed in these sentences.

1. Eliza has a chance to go to one of the following places the mountains the desert or the beach

2. The directions list the following needs pencils ink papers ruler and books

3. The continent of north america is bordered by the atlantic ocean and the pacific ocean

4. The lofty rocky mountains stretch along the western coast from alaska to panama

5. The japanese have an ancient culture

6. We can get a bus at 1145 am or 1230 pm